PRINCIPLES OF
MATHEMATICAL
LOGIC

BY

D. HILBERT AND W. ACKERMANN

TRANSLATED FROM THE GERMAN BY

LEWIS M. HAMMOND • GEORGE G. LECKIE • F. STEINHARDT

Professor of Philosophy   Professor of Philosophy   Columbia University
University of Virginia   Emory University

EDITED AND WITH NOTES BY
ROBERT E. LUCE
Assistant Professor of Mathematics
Rutgers University

CHELSEA PUBLISHING COMPANY
NEW YORK

EDITOR'S PREFACE

This translation of the *Grundzüge der Theoretischen Logik* of Hilbert and Ackermann has been made from the second German edition, which was published in 1938 and has since enjoyed the status, assuredly well-merited, of a classic text in the field of mathematical logic. Those who have cooperated in the translation have sought both to give an exact English rendering of the sense and intent of the original text and also, so far as possible in a different language, to reproduce something of its manner and style. It has nevertheless been judged necessary to depart in some respects from the letter of the German text at places where, in the light of the general advance in precision of logical terminology since the text was written, its formulations now seem ambiguous or otherwise imperfect, and especially at places where technical criticism of the text itself has shown it to be in error. It is one of the purposes of this preface to call the reader's attention to these changes, for which the editor must assume responsibility.

In addition to the correction of a few typographical errors, a number of minor changes have been made throughout the text in correction of the recurrent carelessness of the authors in maintaining a strict distinction (according to present standards) between expressions and the objects designated by them; but changes of this kind have been in every case very slight and have been made only when they seemed necessary in order to avoid serious ambiguity or terminological inconsistency. The reader will observe in this connection that the translators, like the authors, have adopted the customary convention, although without explicit statement thereof, that the symbols and formulas of a logical calculus (object language), when mentioned, or spoken about, in the metalinguistic discussion, may be used autonymously, *i.e.* as names for themselves. And indeed this convention is extended to cover mention of the special symbols (such as the German letters) of the metalanguage as well.

iii

The first of the more serious errors which critical examination of the German text has revealed is one of omission: namely, the authors failed to include an essential condition relative to bound variables in their statement of the rule of substitution for predicate variables [Rule $a3$), pp. 69f. of the translation]. This error was pointed out by Professor Alonzo Church in his monograph of 1944 (*Introduction to Mathematical Logic*) and has been corrected by the insertion of a clause embodying the amendment which he suggested.

A second important difficulty concerns the introduction to the argument of Gödel's completeness proof for the predicate calculus. The inadequacy of the authors' formulation at this point was shown by Professor W. V. Quine in his review of the second German edition at the time of its original appearance.[1] The difficulty is the following: The authors state, in effect, that since they have proved that for every formula of the predicate calculus a formula in Skolem normal form can be found such that either both formulas are provable or both are not provable, they are free to restrict themselves, in carrying out the desired completeness proof, to showing that all universally valid formulas in Skolem normal form are provable. But the conclusion which they draw here would seem to be a *non-sequitur*, since they have nowhere shown that the formula in Skolem normal form corresponding to a given universally valid formula must also be universally valid. Therefore, in the text of the translation a brief paragraph (*viz.* the final paragraph of § 8) has been inserted indicating a method of proof by which the reader may fill in this gap in the argument.of the completeness proof, and the inadequate statement at the beginning of Gödel's argument has been amended accordingly.

The third and most considerable departure in the translation from the original text again concerns the development of Gödel's completeness proof, but this time consists in replacing the erroneous proof of part (A) of Gödel's argument by a corrected proof (pp. 98f). In connection with this corrected proof, the editor is again indebted for suggestions to the writings of Professor

---

[1] The Journal of Symbolic Logic, Vol. 3 (1938), p. 84.

Church, specifically to his proof of the same proposition in his monograph of 1944 (pp. 75f) as subsequently revised in the review of the monograph in the Journal of Symbolic Logic [Vol. 10 (1945) p. 20].

Finally, the editor has added a small number of notes, some of which appear at the back of the book, in supplementation of the translated text. The purpose of the appended notes is to explain various terminological usages in the translation, particularly with a view to helping the student to whom the subject of logic is new and who may wish to correlate his study of this work with his readings in other texts.

In concluding this preface, the editor wishes on behalf of the translators and on his own behalf to thank Mr. J. Schwartz for his kindness in making available for purposes of comparison the manuscript of an independent translation of the same work which he had prepared. We are gratefully indebted to Mr. Schwartz for many valuable suggestions and improvements in expression.

New Brunswick, N. J.

Robert E. Luce

PREFACE TO THE FIRST (GERMAN) EDITION

The present work treats mathematical logic (also called symbolic logic, logistic, or the algebra of logic) in a form that I have developed and used in my university lectures on the fundamental principles of mathematics (*Principles of Mathematics*, Winter Session 1917-18; *Logical Calculus*, Winter Session 1920; *Foundations of Mathematics*, Winter Session 1921-22). In the preparation of these lectures I have had considerable aid and advice from my colleague P. Bernays; he has also written the lectures up most carefully. The material thus obtained has been used and supplemented, to give the present arrangement and definitive presentation of the entire subject matter, by W. Ackermann, a student of mine who has since distinguished himself by important papers of his own on the foundations of mathematics.

This book is intended to serve at the same time as an introduction to and preparation for a further book, which P. Bernays and I plan to publish soon and which treats the foundations of mathematics by the method I have expounded—again with the active cooperation of P. Bernays—in a series of articles (*Neubegründung der Mathematik*, Abhandlungen des mathematischen Seminars der Hamburgischen Universität, Vol. 1, p. 157 (1922) ; *Die logischen Grundlagen der Mathematik*, Math. Ann. Vol. 88, p. 151 (1922) ; *Über das Unendliche*, Math. Ann. Vol. 95 p. 161 (1925)).

Göttingen, January 16, 1928

Hilbert

PREFACE TO THE SECOND (GERMAN) EDITION

The second edition of the present work retains the arrangement and form of the first edition throughout. However, the progress which has been made in the subject since the appearance of the First Edition has made it necessary to go over the book in detail and to include various improvements and additions. This has been done without going beyond the limits set for the book.

The first and second chapters are essentially unchanged, except that recent investigations of the axiomatic basis of the sentential calculus have been briefly taken into account in the first chapter. A more extensive presentation of the class calculus in the second chapter, which might have been desirable for its own sake, was not given, since this calculus occupies, after all, an isolated position in the overall arrangement of the book. In the third chapter, the formulation of the rules of inference for the predicate calculus, which was not sufficiently precise, has been improved. Proofs of the independence and completeness of the system of axioms used there have been newly added, and the section on the decision problem has been supplemented by incorporating recent results. It was possible to shorten the fourth chapter inasmuch as it was no longer necessary to go into Whitehead and Russell's ramified theory of types, since it seems to have been generally abandoned. On the other hand, the structure of the predicate calculus of second order and of the calculus of order ω has been considerably improved and rounded out.

The terminology has been adapted to that of the *Grundlagen der Mathematik* by Hilbert and Bernays. For example, the term "functional calculus" has been everywhere replaced by "predicate calculus." Following general logical usage, the expressions "logical sum" and "logical product" have been changed throughout to "conjunction" and "disjunction."

For much helpful advice I am especially indebted to Professor P. Bernays of Zürich, who also read the galley proofs. I am also grateful for various suggestions to Mr. G. Gentzen of Göttingen, who also examined the manuscript, as well as to Messrs. Arnold Schmidt of Marburg and H. Scholz of Münster. To all of them I offer my most cordial thanks.

Burgsteinfurt, November, 1937

W. Ackermann

TABLE OF CONTENTS

xi

III. The Restricted Predicate Calculus

IV. The Extended Predicate Calculus

INTRODUCTION

Mathematical logic, also called *symbolic logic* or *logistic,* is an extension of the formal method of mathematics to the field of logic. It employs for logic a symbolic language like that which has long been in use to express mathematical relations. In mathematics it would nowadays be considered Utopian to think of using only ordinary language in constructing a mathematical discipline. The great advances in mathematics since antiquity, for instance in algebra, have been dependent to a large extent upon success in finding a usable and efficient symbolism.

The purpose of the symbolic language in mathematical logic is to achieve in logic what it has achieved in mathematics, namely, an exact scientific treatment of its subject-matter. The logical relations which hold with regard to judgments, concepts, etc., are represented by formulas whose interpretation is free from the ambiguities so common in ordinary language. The transition from statements to their logical consequences, as occurs in the drawing of conclusions, is analysed into its primitive elements, and appears as a formal transformation of the initial formulas in accordance with certain rules, similar to the rules of algebra; logical thinking is reflected in a logical calculus. This calculus makes possible a successful attack on problems whose nature precludes their solution by purely intuitive logical thinking. Among these, for instance, is the problem of characterizing those statements which can be deduced from given premises.

In the last few decades the logical calculus has acquired added significance, in that it has been developed into an indispensable instrument for investigating the foundations of mathematics.

The first clear idea of a mathematical logic was formulated by Leibniz. The first results were obtained by A. de Morgan (1806-1876) and G. Boole (1815-1864). The entire later development goes back to Boole. Among his successors, W. S. Jevons (1835-1882) and especially C. S. Peirce (1839-1914) enriched the young science. Ernst Schröder systematically organized and

1

supplemented the various results of his predecessors in his *Vorlesungen über die Algebra der Logik* (1890-1895), which represents a certain completion of the series of developments proceeding from Boole.

In part independently of the development of the Boole-Schröder algebra, symbolic logic received a new impetus from the need of mathematics for an exact foundation and strict axiomatic treatment. G. Frege published his *Begriffsschrift* in 1879 and his *Grundgesetze der Arithmetik* in 1893-1903. G. Peano and his co-workers began in 1894 the publication of the *Formulaire de Mathématiques*, in which all the mathematical disciplines were to be presented in terms of the logical calculus. A high point of this development is the appearance of the *Principia Mathematica* (1910-1913) by A. N. Whitehead and B. Russell. Most recently Hilbert, in a series of papers and university lectures, has used the logical calculus to find a new way of building up mathematics which makes it possible to recognize the consistency of the postulates adopted. The first comprehensive account of these researches has appeared in the *Grundlagen der Mathematik* (1934-1939), by D. Hilbert and P. Bernays.

CHAPTER I

THE SENTENTIAL CALCULUS

A first and indispensable part of mathematical logic consists of the so-called sentential calculus (calculus of sentences). By a sentence is to be understood any expression concerning which it is meaningful to say that its content is true or false. Examples of sentences are: "Mathematics is a science," "snow is black," "9 is a prime number." In the sentential calculus we are not concerned with the inner logical structure of sentences, such as is exhibited, say, in the relation between subject and predicate, but consider the sentences as wholes in their logical combination with other sentences.

§ 1. Introduction of the Fundamental Logical Connectives

Sentences can be combined in a definite manner to form new sentences. For example, from the two sentences "2 is less than 3," "snow is black," one can construct the new sentences: "2 is less than 3 *and* snow is black," "2 is less than 3 *or* snow is black," "*if* 2 is less than 3, *then* snow is black." Finally, from "2 is less than 3" one can construct the new sentence, "2 is *not* less than 3," which expresses the logical opposite of the first sentence.

These combinations of sentences are rendered verbally by the words *"and," "or," "not," "if-then."*

We wish now to render these fundamental combinations of sentences by a suitable symbolism. We shall employ capital italic letters $X, Y, Z, U, \ldots$ to stand for sentences. To indicate the logical combination of sentences, we shall introduce the following five symbols:

1. $\bar{X}$ (read *"not X"*) stands for the opposite or contradictory of X, that is, for that sentence which is true if X is false and which is false if X is true.

2. $X \& Y$ (read *"X and Y"*) stands for the sentence which is true if and only if both X and Y are true.

3. $X \vee Y$ (read *"X or Y"*) stands for the sentence which is true if and only if at least one of the two sentences X, Y is true.

4. $X \to Y$ (read *"if X then Y"*) stands for the sentence which is false if and only if X is true and Y is false.

5. $X \sim Y$ (read *"X if and only if Y"*), also written $X \leftrightarrow Y$ or $X \rightleftarrows Y$, stands for the sentence which is true if and only if X and Y are both true or both false. $X \sim Y$ means, therefore, that X and Y have the same truth value.

With regard to 3., note that the "or" in the combination "X or Y" must not be confused with the exclusive "or" in the sense of the Latin *aut* ("X or Y but not both"). It rather has the meaning of the inclusive "or" in the sense of the Latin *vel* ("X or Y or both"), *i.e.* the possibility of both X and Y being true simultaneously is admitted.[1]

The compound sentence "if X then Y" is not to be taken to indicate a relation of premise and conclusion or of cause and effect. Rather, the sentence $X \to Y$ is always true if X is a false sentence and also if Y is a true sentence.

Thus, for example, the following sentences are to be regarded as true:

If 2 times 2 equals 4, *then* snow is white.

If 2 times 2 equals 5, *then* snow is white.

If 2 times 2 equals 5, *then* snow is black.

On the other hand, the sentence *"if 2 times 2 equals 4, then* snow is black" would be false. Nevertheless, the relation $X \to Y$ has this in common with the relation of premise and conclusion, that in the case of the truth of $X \to Y$, the truth of Y can be inferred from that of X.

The assertion of $X \sim Y$ does not have the sense that X and Y have the same meaning or significance; rather, the assertion holds

---

[1] The exclusive "either ... or" can also be expressed by a combination of the fundamental symbols. "Either X or Y" is the negation of $X \sim Y$, written $\overline{X \sim Y}$. [The American reader may find it useful to recall that the inclusive sense of "or," adopted as the intended meaning in 3., is that sometimes expressed, especially in juristic language, by the barbarism "and/or."—*Ed.*]

with respect to any two true sentences and also any two false ones. *E.g.* the two sentences

$$(2 \text{ and } 2 \text{ make } 4) \sim (\text{snow is white})$$

and

$$(2 \text{ is greater than } 3) \sim (\text{snow is black})$$

are true.

Finally, the following general remark is very important. In accordance with our definition of the fundamental logical connectives, *the truth or falsehood of a sentential combination depends solely upon the truth or falsehood of the sentences entering into the combination, and not upon their content.* If for abbreviation we let T stand for a true sentence and F for a false one, then *e.g.* the connective $\rightarrow$ is characterized thus: The sentences $T \rightarrow T$, $F \rightarrow T$, and $F \rightarrow F$ are true, but $T \rightarrow F$ is false. For the connective &, $T \& T$ is true; $T \& F$, $F \& T$, and $F \& F$ are all false. Further, $T \vee T$, $T \vee F$, $F \vee T$ are true; $F \vee F$, false. The connective $\sim$ is characterized by the fact that $T \sim T$ and $F \sim F$ are true, whereas $T \sim F$ and $F \sim T$ are false. Finally, $\bar{T}$ is false, $\bar{F}$ true. Accordingly, we are justified in considering the fundamental connectives as truth functions: *i.e.* as definite functions for which only T and F are considered as arguments and as functional values.

As a formal characterization of the operations which have been introduced, it should be noted that only negation $(\bar{X})$ is a one-place operation, while all the others are two-place.

§ 2. Equivalence; Dispensability of Fundamental Connectives

By repeated application of the fundamental connectives, more complicated sentential combinations can be constructed from any given sentences. For example, the compound sentence $((X \rightarrow Y) \& (Y \rightarrow Z)) \& (X \vee Z)$ is obtained in this way from the original sentences X, Y, Z. Any such combination of sentences expresses a definite truth function, just as the fundamental combinations do. In the above combination of sentences we have for X, Y, and Z the eight possible truth-value distributions: T,T,T;

T,T,F; T,F,T; T,F,F; F,T,T; F,T,F; F,F,T; F,F,F. With each of these value distributions there is correlated by means of

$$((X \to Y) \ \& \ (Y \to Z)) \ \& \ (X \lor Z)$$

either the value T or the value F. For example, with the value distribution F,T,F there is correlated the value F. For, according to the definition of the fundamental combinations, we may replace

$$((F \to T) \ \& \ (T \to F)) \ \& \ (F \lor F)$$

by (T & F) & F, and this in turn by F & F and, finally, by F.

It should be noted that different combinations of the fundamental connectives may have the same meaning, $i.e.$, express the same truth function. Thus, $\bar{X}$ has the same meaning as X; the double negative is the same as an affirmative. In fact, $\bar{\bar{X}}$, just like X, yields the value T when T is substituted for X, and the value F when F is substituted for X. Combinations such as these, with the same meaning, we shall call "equivalent" in what follows. For abbreviation we write[1]

(1) $$\bar{\bar{X}} \ \text{eq.} \ X.$$

In the following we shall give a series of further equivalences. There appears, first, an analogy in the way the symbols & and v operate with the way the symbols $+$ and $\times$ operate in algebra. We have, namely, the following equivalences:

(2) $\qquad\qquad X \ \& \ Y \quad \text{eq.} \quad Y \ \& \ X,$
(3) $\qquad\quad X \ \& \ (Y \ \& \ Z) \quad \text{eq.} \quad (X \ \& \ Y) \ \& \ Z,$
(4) $\qquad\qquad X \lor Y \quad \text{eq.} \quad Y \lor X,$
(5) $\qquad\quad X \lor (Y \lor Z) \quad \text{eq.} \quad (X \lor Y) \lor Z,$
(6) $\qquad\quad X \lor (Y \ \& \ Z) \quad \text{eq.} \quad (X \lor Y) \ \& \ (X \lor Z).$

It follows from the above that the truth of these (and all other) equivalences can be verified in the following way: Take all possible combinations which can be obtained by replacing the original sentences with T's and F's; and check that for each individual combination both sides of the equivalence under consideration yield in each case the same truth value. This verification is left to the reader.

---

[1] It should be noted that the abbreviation "eq." used here does not belong to our set of logical symbols.

From the equivalences (2) through (6) a *commutative*, an *associative*, and a *distributive* law may be derived. On account of this analogy with algebra, $X \& Y$ has been called the *logical sum*, and $X \vee Y$ the *logical product*. It follows from the laws just stated that we may "multiply out" and that we may "factor out" a common factor in logical expressions, just as in algebra. Incidentally, we might just as well have called $X \& Y$ the logical product, and $X \vee Y$ the logical sum; indeed this nomenclature is the one more commonly employed in logic. In contrast to algebra there is a *second distributive law*, namely

(7) $X \& (Y \vee Z)$ eq. $(X \& Y) \vee (X \& Z)$.

The following example illustrates the second distributive law. Take the weather forecast, "It will rain today, and tomorrow or the next day the sun will shine." The same assertion may also be expressed thus: "It will rain today and tomorrow the sun will shine, or it will rain today and the day after tomorrow the sun will shine."

Since logical usage varies regarding the terms "sum" and "product" we generally prefer to avoid these expressions. Instead, we shall call $X \& Y$ the *conjunction* of X and Y, and $X \vee Y$ the *disjunction* of X and Y. $X \rightarrow Y$ is usually called *implication*.

On account of the commutative and associative laws, conjunctions and disjunctions with several components may be written without parentheses. For the further elimination of parentheses, we shall adopt the convention that there is an order of precedence among the connectives, according to which $\rightarrow$ and $\sim$ have precedence over &, and & in turn over v. The symbol v may be omitted, just like the symbol $\times$ in algebra.

For simplifying conjunctions and disjunctions, the following equivalences are essential:

(8) $X \& X$ eq. X,
(9) $X \vee X$ eq. X.

Thus in a conjunction or disjunction in which one component appears several times, it need be written only once. In like manner, the following equivalences often serve to replace more complicated combinations of sentences with simpler ones:

(10)	$X \& \mathrm{T}$ eq. X,
(11)	$X \& \mathrm{F}$ eq. F.

Formula (10) says that a true component of a conjunction may always be left out; (11), that a conjunction in which a false sentence occurs is false.

Correspondingly, for disjunction we have:

(12)	$X \vee \mathrm{T}$ eq. T,
(13)	$X \vee \mathrm{F}$ eq. X.

A disjunction is true if it contains a true component. A false component may be omitted from a disjunction.

We have similar relations in the case of implication also:

(14)	$\mathrm{T} \to X$ eq. X,
(15)	$\mathrm{F} \to X$ eq. T.

An implication with a true first component is equivalent to its second component. An implication with a false first component always constitutes a true sentence.

Finally, for the connective "if and only if," we have:

(16)	$X \sim \mathrm{T}$ eq. X,
(17)	$X \sim \mathrm{F}$ eq. $\overline{X}$.

When negation is joined with & and v, the following relation is essential:

$$(18) \qquad \overline{X \& Y} \text{ eq. } \overline{X} \vee \overline{Y}.$$

For example, let X stand for the sentence "The triangle $\triangle$ is a right triangle" and let Y mean "The triangle $\triangle$ is isosceles." To the combination $X \& Y$ then corresponds the sentence: "The triangle $\triangle$ is a right triangle and the triangle $\triangle$ is isosceles." Its contradictory opposite is the sentence: "The triangle $\triangle$ is not a right triangle or the triangle $\triangle$ is not isosceles," and this sentence is rendered by $\overline{X} \vee \overline{Y}$.

Likewise,

$$(19) \qquad \overline{X \vee Y} \text{ eq. } \overline{X} \& \overline{Y}$$

holds.

For example, it is required in a mathematics examination that the candidate be prepared in at least one of the two fields, arithmetic and geometry. Let X stand for the sentence: "The candidate is proficient in arithmetic," and let Y stand for "The candidate is proficient in geometry." The requirements of the examination are fulfilled by the candidate if $X \vee Y$ is true. But if the candidate fails the examination, if we are thus confronted with the opposite of $X \vee Y$, then we have: "The candidate is not proficient in arithmetic and he is not proficient in geometry," which is rendered by $\overline{X} \,\&\, \overline{Y}$.

Further equivalences are obtained involving the symbols $\rightarrow$ and $\sim$.

Since the sentence $X \rightarrow Y$ means that it is not true that X is true and Y is false at the same time, there follows:

(20) $X \rightarrow Y$ eq. $\overline{X \,\&\, \overline{Y}}$.

By using (18), $\overline{X \,\&\, \overline{Y}}$ can also be written $\overline{X} \vee \overline{\overline{Y}}$ or, according to (1), $\overline{X} \vee Y$. Thus we also have:

(21) $X \rightarrow Y$ eq. $\overline{X} \vee Y$.

If in this equivalence we take $\overline{X}$ instead of X, and use the fact that $\overline{\overline{X}}$ eq. X, we obtain the new relation

(22) $X \vee Y$ eq. $\overline{X} \rightarrow Y$.

According to (20), $\overline{Y} \rightarrow \overline{X}$ eq. $\overline{\overline{Y} \,\&\, \overline{\overline{X}}}$. For this we may, by (1), substitute $\overline{\overline{Y} \,\&\, X}$; by (2), $\overline{X \,\&\, \overline{Y}}$; and, by (20), $X \rightarrow Y$. Thus we have:

(23) $X \rightarrow Y$ eq. $\overline{Y} \rightarrow \overline{X}$.

Further, if both sentences $X \rightarrow Y$ and $Y \rightarrow X$ are true, this means it is not true that X is true and Y false at the same time, or that Y is true and X false at the same time. The sentence $(X \rightarrow Y) \,\&\, (Y \rightarrow X)$ thus means that X and Y both have the same truth value. In other words, the equivalence

(24) $X \sim Y$ eq. $(X \rightarrow Y) \,\&\, (Y \rightarrow X)$

holds.

It follows immediately from the meaning of the connective $\sim$ that

(25) $X \sim Y$ eq. $Y \sim X$,
(26) $X \sim Y$ eq. $\overline{X} \sim \overline{Y}$.

It follows further from (19) and (18), by taking the negation of both sides of the equivalence and using the fact that, according to (1), the double negation may be omitted:

(27) $X \lor Y$ eq. $\overline{\overline{X} \& \overline{Y}}$,

(28) $X \& Y$ eq. $\overline{\overline{X} \lor \overline{Y}}$.

These equivalences show that *if we want to render a given combination of sentences by means of the symbols introduced, we have more than one way of doing so.* This suggests the possibility that *some of the fundamental logical connectives are dispensable.* Such is actually the case. Thus it follows from (24) that the sign $\sim$ can be dispensed with, since the combination $X \sim Y$ can be rendered by $\to$ and $\&$. It follows further from (20) and (27) that $\to$ and $\lor$ are also dispensable; *i.e.*, $\&$ and $\overline{}$ are sufficient. Likewise, (21) and (28) show that $\lor$ and $\overline{}$ also suffice. Similarly, $\to$ and $\overline{}$ suffice, for by (28), $\&$ can be expressed by $\lor$ and $\overline{}$, and by (22), $\lor$ can be expressed by $\to$ and $\overline{}$.

Frege bases his formulation upon the connectives $\to$ and $\overline{}$; Russell prefers for this purpose $\lor$ and $\overline{}$. (They use somewhat different symbols, however.) It is probably most natural to start with the connectives $\&$ and $\overline{}$ as primitive, as Brentano does in his theory of judgment. The use of the three signs $\&$, $\lor$, and $\overline{}$ is especially suitable, since equivalences (2) through (6) then give a particularly simple way of calculating with logical expressions.

Not all combinations can be rendered by $\sim$ and $\overline{}$. Thus $X \& Y$ cannot be expressed in terms of these symbols. To prove this, let us assume that we form combinations with only two elementary sentences X and Y. Let us then consider the eight sentences

$$X; Y; \overline{X}; \overline{Y}; X \sim X; X \sim \overline{X}; X \sim Y; X \sim \overline{Y}.$$

Any sentence obtained by negating one of these eight, or by combining any two of them by $\sim$, is itself equivalent to one of the eight. For example, $(X \sim Y) \sim Y$ eq. X; $(X \sim Y) \sim (X \sim Y)$ eq. $X \sim X$, etc. Since the elementary sentences X and Y themselves occur among the eight sentences, it follows that any sentence compounded out of X and Y by applying only $\sim$ and $\overline{}$ is itself equivalent to one of the eight sentences. But $X \& Y$

is equivalent to none of these eight sentences. Should there be a combination of sentences compounded only by means of $\sim$ and $-$ and equivalent to X & Y, containing sentences $Z, U, \ldots, T$, in addition to X and Y, then the equivalence would have to hold also if X were substituted for every one of the sentences $Z, U, \ldots, T$. This leads back to the preceding case.

Negation is indispensable for expressing combinations of sentences. For example, $\overline{X}$ cannot be expressed without the employment of negation. For, all expressions constructed by applying &, v, $\rightarrow$, $\sim$ to the indeterminate symbol X yield sentences which are true provided X is true, whereas $\overline{X}$ has the truth value opposite to that of X.

It is worth noting that the connective v can be expressed by $\rightarrow$ alone, without the use of negation. For we have

$$X \text{ v } Y \quad \text{eq.} \quad (X \rightarrow Y) \rightarrow Y.$$

Such an expression is not possible for X & Y.

As a curiosity we mention the fact that a single logical sign suffices, as Sheffer has shown. He used as the only fundamental combination X/Y, in words: "Either not X or not Y." X/X then means the same as $\overline{X}$. $(X/X)/(Y/Y)$ is equivalent to $\overline{X}/\overline{Y}$, i.e. X v Y. Since v and $-$ can be expressed by Sheffer's stroke, the same holds for the other fundamental connectives.

Finally, we mention the following equivalences as of importance for representing the relation of having the same truth value:

(29) $X \sim Y \quad \text{eq.} \quad \overline{X} \text{ v } Y \; \& \; \overline{Y} \text{ v } X,$
(30) $X \sim Y \quad \text{eq.} \quad (X \& Y)(\overline{X} \& \overline{Y}).$

(29) follows from (24) by expressing the connective $\rightarrow$ in terms of v and $-$, according to (21). (30) follows immediately from the meaning of $\sim$.

§ 3. Normal Form for Logical Expressions

Up to this point we have seen how new sentences can be formed by one or more applications of the connectives &, v, $\rightarrow$, $-$ to certain elementary sentences which are symbolized by $X, Y, Z, \ldots$. The equivalences set forth in the preceding section show us that there may be a multiplicity of expressions (having the same meaning with respect to content) for a combination of elementary sentences, so that one can pass from one to the other of the expressions at will. Now it is noteworthy that *any combination of sentences can be brought into a certain normal form by means of equivalence transformations*; and indeed this normal form consists of a conjunction of disjunctions in which each component of the disjunction is either an elementary sentence or the negation of one.

On the basis of the equivalences set forth, we establish the following rules for the transformation of logical expressions:

a1) *Calculations with the symbols & and v follow the associative, commutative, and distributive laws, as in algebra.*

a2) *For $\bar{\bar{X}}$ we may substitute X* (and vice versa).

a3) *We may write $\bar{X}$ v $\bar{Y}$ for $\overline{X \& Y}$, and $\bar{X} \& \bar{Y}$ for $\overline{X v Y}$* (and vice versa).

a4) *We may substitute $\bar{X}$ v Y for X → Y, and $\bar{X}Y$ & $\bar{Y}X$ for X ∼ Y* (and vice versa).[1]

The transformation is effected thus: First, by employing Rule a4), we can substitute for any expression an equivalent one which no longer contains the symbols → and ∼. The resulting expression is then entirely in terms of the three symbols &, v, and —. By successive applications of Rule a3), the negation signs can be brought farther and farther inside, until finally they stand only over the elementary sentences. For example, from

$$(\overline{XY \& \bar{Y}}) \text{ v } (Z \& Y)$$

we have first

$$(\overline{XY \& \bar{Y}}) \& (\overline{Z \& Y}),$$

then by another application of a3):

$$\overline{\hat{XY} \text{ v } \bar{\bar{Y}} \& \bar{Z} \text{ v } \bar{Y}}$$

and finally

$$(\bar{X} \& \bar{Y}) \text{ } \bar{\bar{Y}} \& \bar{Z}\bar{Y}.$$

The resulting expression is thus composed of negated and un-negated elementary sentences connected by & and v. Now by

---

[1] Here, and generally in what follows, we employ the convenient notational device already mentioned, *viz.*, the omission of the symbol v.

applying the distributive law, one obtains, in our example:

$$\bar{X}\bar{Y} \,\&\, \bar{Y}\bar{Y} \,\&\, \bar{Z}\bar{Y}.$$

Now substituting, by a2), X for $\bar{\bar{X}}$, $\bar{X}$ for $\bar{\bar{\bar{X}}}$, etc., the expression is brought into normal form.

As a second example, let us consider the expression

$$(X \rightarrow Y) \sim (\bar{Y} \rightarrow \bar{X}).$$

Eliminating the sign $\rightarrow$ according to a4), we have

$$\bar{X}Y \sim \bar{\bar{Y}}\bar{X}.$$

Substituting Y for $\bar{\bar{Y}}$, we have

$$\bar{X}Y \sim Y\bar{X}.$$

Once more applying a4), we obtain

$$(\overline{\bar{X}Y})\,Y\bar{X} \,\&\, (\overline{Y\bar{X}})\,\bar{X}Y,$$
$$(\bar{\bar{X}} \,\&\, \bar{Y})\,Y\bar{X} \,\&\, (\bar{Y} \,\&\, \bar{\bar{X}})\,\bar{X}Y \qquad \text{[by a3)].}$$

Substituting X for $\bar{\bar{X}}$, we obtain

$$(X \,\&\, \bar{Y})\,Y\bar{X} \,\&\, (\bar{Y} \,\&\, X)\bar{X}Y.$$

By applying the distributive law, we then have

$$XY\bar{X} \,\&\, \bar{Y}Y\bar{X} \,\&\, \bar{Y}\bar{X}Y \,\&\, X\bar{X}Y.$$

This is a normal form of $(X \rightarrow Y) \sim (\bar{Y} \rightarrow \bar{X})$.

We note, incidentally, that the normal form belonging to a combination of sentences is not unique. For example, by (29) there belongs to $X \sim Y$ on the one hand the normal form $\bar{X}Y \,\&\, \bar{Y}X$. On the other hand, by applying the distributive law to the right hand side of (30), we have

$$X\bar{X} \,\&\, X\bar{Y} \,\&\, Y\bar{X} \,\&\, Y\bar{Y}.$$

§ 4. Characterization of Logically True Combinations of Sentences

The truth or falsehood of a combination of sentences constructed in a definite way from elementary sentences $X_1, X_2, \ldots, X_n$ by means of the logical symbols $\&$, v, $\rightarrow$, $\sim$, $^{—}$ depends only upon the distribution of truth and falsehood among the elementary sentences. The truth value of a sentential combination remains unchanged when one of the component sentences is replaced by one having the same truth value. Thus it follows that the symbol $\sim$ plays in our calculus a role similar to that of the symbol $=$ in algebra.

It is now the first task of logic *to find those combinations of sentences which are logically true, i.e. true independently of the truth values of the elementary sentences.*

Since for any given logical expression we can find an equivalent one in normal form, the solution of this problem is only a matter of *determining when an expression in normal form represents a logically true combination of sentences.* This determination is arrived at by means of the following rules which are easily verified.

b1) $X\bar{X}$ is logically true.

b2)   If X is true, and Y is any sentence whatsoever, then XY is also true.

b3)   If X is true and Y is true, then $X \& Y$ is also true.

It is to be understood that for the X and Y in these rules we may substitute any sentences or combinations of sentences.

In accordance with Rules b1), b2), b3), and a1), it may be seen that *all expressions in normal form are true which have the characteristic that in each disjunction there occurs at least one of the elementary sentences together with its negation.* It follows immediately from the meaning of negation and of the connectives "and" and "or" that such an expression constitutes a true sentence, whatever may be the content of the elementary sentences. Moreover, these are the only expressions which are logically true. For if every elementary sentence in some conjunct[1] —which is itself a disjunction—of a normal form occurs as a factor either only un-negated or only negated, then this disjunction can be made into a false sentence by replacing each un-negated symbol by a false sentence and each negated symbol by

---

[1] The term "conjunct" is employed here and in what follows to designate a component of a conjunction. Similarly, "disjunct" will be employed to designate a component of a disjunction.—*Ed.*

a true sentence. Then a conjunct of the normal form is a false sentence, and consequently the entire expression yields a false sentence, independently of what is substituted for the sentential symbols as yet undetermined.

We shall give some examples to show how sentences may be verified as being logically true by the use of the above method.

1. $X \sim X$.

Transforming by Rule a4) gives:

$$\overline{X}X \,\&\, \overline{X}X.$$

This expression (in normal form) contains an elementary sentence and its negation in each conjunct, and is therefore true.

2. $X \,\&\, Y \to X$.

The transformation yields:

$$\overline{X \,\&\, Y} \text{ v } X \qquad\qquad \text{[by a4)]},$$
$$\overline{X}\,\overline{Y}\,X \qquad\qquad \text{[by a3)]}.$$

This disjunction contains X and $\overline{X}$, and hence is true.

3. $(X \,\&\, (X \to Y)) \to Y$.

We obtain

$$\overline{X \,\&\, \overline{X}Y} \text{ v } Y \qquad\qquad \text{[by double application of a4)]},$$
$$\overline{X}(\overline{\overline{X}} \,\&\, \overline{Y})\,Y \qquad\qquad \text{[by a3)]},$$
$$\overline{X}\overline{\overline{X}}Y \,\&\, \overline{X}\overline{Y}Y \qquad\qquad \text{[by a1)]},$$
$$\overline{X}XY \,\&\, \overline{X}\overline{Y}Y \qquad\qquad \text{[by a2)]}.$$

The first disjunction contains X and $\overline{X}$, the second, Y and $\overline{Y}$, as factors. Thus $(X \,\&\, (X \to Y)) \to Y$ is a logically true sentential combination.

§ 5. The Principle of Duality

A remark which is important for the characterization of our calculus is based on Rule a3). From that rule it follows that *given an expression which is formed from elementary sentences and their negations by means of conjunction and disjunction alone, we can obtain its negation by interchanging the symbols & and v, and replacing each elementary sentence by its negation.*

We can make the following application of this. Let an expression of the form $\mathfrak{A} \sim \mathfrak{B}$, or as we also say, a logical equation, be established as logically true. (We use German letters to designate combinations of sentences whose exact formal structure is left undetermined, and we also use them for abbreviation.) Since $\mathfrak{A} \sim \mathfrak{B}$ has the same truth value as $\overline{\mathfrak{A}} \sim \overline{\mathfrak{B}}$, we obtain another true expression by forming the negation of both sides of the equation. Now if both sides of the equation are formed from the elementary sentences and their negations by means of conjunction and disjunction only, we can apply the rule just mentioned. We obtain therefrom a formula which arises from the original equation $\mathfrak{A} \sim \mathfrak{B}$ by interchanging the signs & and v, and replacing each elementary sentence with its negation. Since this formula is logically true, it remains so if we replace each elementary sentence by its negation. In so doing, however, we cancel out the original replacement of the elementary sentences with their negations.

Thus we obtain the following *Principle of Duality*: *From a formula* $\mathfrak{A} \sim \mathfrak{B}$ *which is logically true, and both of whose sides are formed from elementary sentences and their negations by conjunction and disjunction only, there results another true equation by the interchange of & and* v.

Thus, for example,

$$X(Y \& Z) \sim XY \& XZ$$

is logically true. This formula expresses the first distributive law. From it is derived, in accordance with the principle of duality, the formula

$$X \& YZ \sim (X \& Y)(X \& Z),$$

which is also true and which expresses the second distributive law.

In the same way, the true formula

$$(X \& \overline{X})Y \sim Y$$

is associated, according to the principle of duality, with the formula

$$X\overline{X} \& Y \sim Y,$$

which is likewise true.

§ 6. The Disjunctive Normal Form for Logical Expressions

There is an important application of the rule for forming the negation of a formula. We have seen that every logical expression can be brought into a normal form. This normal form consists of a conjunction of disjunctions, where each disjunct of every disjunction is either a negated or an un-negated elementary sentence. The tranformation of an expression into its normal form is effected by means of Rules a1) through a4). There is, in addition, still a *second normal form*, which consists of a disjunction of conjunctions. Each conjunct is a negated or an un-negated elementary sentence. We call this normal form *"disjunctive,"* and the preceding one, *"conjunctive,"* to distinguish between them.

The transformation of an expression into disjunctive normal form can be effected in the following way: Negate the original expression, then bring it into conjunctive normal form, and finally form the negation thereof by means of our rule.

One can also make use of the fact that, as far as Rules a1) through a4) are concerned, conjunction and disjunction play dual roles.

Just as one can determine by inspection whether or not an expression in conjunctive normal form is logically true, so also by means of the disjunctive normal form one can determine whether or not it is logically false. This is the case if and only if each disjunct contains an elementary sentence together with its negation.

The proof of this follows at once if one reflects that the negation of a disjunctive normal form reduces, by our rule, to a conjunctive normal form, and that a formula is logically false if and only if its negation is logically true.

As an example of the application of the disjunctive normal form, let us consider the sentential combination

$$\overline{X}Y \mathbin{\&} \overline{Y}Z \mathbin{\&} X \mathbin{\&} \overline{Z}.$$

By applying the second distributive law, we get the normal form

$$(\overline{X} \mathbin{\&} \overline{Y} \mathbin{\&} X \mathbin{\&} \overline{Z}) \vee (\overline{X} \mathbin{\&} Z \mathbin{\&} X \mathbin{\&} \overline{Z}) \vee$$
$$(Y \mathbin{\&} \overline{Y} \mathbin{\&} X \mathbin{\&} \overline{Z}) \vee (Y \mathbin{\&} Z \mathbin{\&} X \mathbin{\&} \overline{Z}).$$

Here, each disjunct contains an elementary sentence and its negation; the first two, X and $\overline{X}$; the third, Y and $\overline{Y}$; the fourth, Z and $\overline{Z}$. Thus $\overline{X}Y$ & $\overline{Y}Z$ & X & $\overline{Z}$ constitutes a sentence which is logically false.

The disjunctive normal form has the advantage of special clarity. The individual components of the disjunction indicate the various possible cases in which the given sentential combination holds true. Thus, for example, the disjunctive normal form which belongs to $X \sim Y$ reads $(X \mathbin{\&} Y)$ v $(\overline{X} \mathbin{\&} \overline{Y})$, and this enables us to recognize that X and Y must either both be true or both be false in order for $X \sim Y$ to be true.

§ 7. The Totality of Combinations Which Can Be Formed from Given Elementary Sentences

A further important remark about the calculus concerns the totality of sentences which can be formed by combination from a finite number of elementary sentences $X_1, X_2, \ldots, X_n$. Here we will consider sentences as distinct only if they are not logically equivalent. With this assumption, the totality consists of only a finite number of sentences.

As mentioned above, a sentence constructed from $X_1, X_2, \ldots, X_n$ is equivalent to another such sentence if and only if both sentences have the same truth value for arbitrary values of $X_1, X_2, \ldots, X_n$. To begin with, for the truth or falsehood of the elementary sentences there are 2^n possibilities, since each individual sentence $X_1, X_2, \ldots, X_n$ can be true or false. Now the truth or falsehood of a sentence compounded from $X_1, X_2, \ldots, X_n$ is determined by checking its truth or falsehood in each of the 2^n cases. Consequently there are exactly $2^{(2^n)}$ distinct sentences which can be compounded from $X_1, X_2, \ldots, X_n$.

The four different sentences constructed from X alone are:

$$X; \overline{X}; X \mathbin{\text{v}} \overline{X}; X \mathbin{\&} \overline{X}.$$

The sixteen different sentences constructed from X and Y are:

$$X; Y; X \mathbin{\&} Y; X \mathbin{\text{v}} Y; X \to Y; Y \to X; X \sim Y; X \mathbin{\text{v}} \overline{X}$$

and their negations

$$\overline{X}; \overline{Y}; \overline{X} \mathbin{\text{v}} \overline{Y}; \overline{X} \mathbin{\&} \overline{Y}; X \mathbin{\&} \overline{Y}; Y \mathbin{\&} \overline{X}; X \sim \overline{Y}; X \mathbin{\&} \overline{X}.$$

Among the $2^{(2^n)}$ sentences, two play a special role, namely, the logically true sentence, expressible, say, by $X_1 \vee \overline{X}_1$ (or $X_1 \sim X_1$), and the logically false sentence expressible by $X_1 \& \overline{X}_1$.

The following theorem gives a formal summary of the distinct sentences constructible from $X_1, X_2, \ldots, X_n$:

Every expression constructed from the elementary sentences $X_1, X_2, \ldots, X_n$ is equivalent to a conjunction which is part of the conjunction obtained when the following expression is developed according to the first distributive law:

$$(X_1 \& \overline{X}_1) \vee (X_2 \& \overline{X}_2) \vee \ldots \vee (X_n \& \overline{X}_n).$$

The sole exceptions are the expressions which are logically true. However, the improper partial conjunction which arises when all components are omitted may be considered as an expression which is logically true. Schröder calls the individual conjuncts of the above expression, when developed, the *constituents* of $X_1, X_2, \ldots, X_n$.

The proof of this assertion runs thus: First, bring the expression constructed from $X_1, \ldots, X_n$ into conjunctive normal form. Since the truth value of an expression remains unchanged when a true conjunct is omitted, it is not necessary to write down any conjunct which contains an X and its negation $\overline{X}$. Employing next the rule that only X need be written for $X \vee X$, it follows that each of the remaining conjuncts is simply a disjunction whose disjuncts are elements, with distinct subscripts, of the series $X_1, \ldots, X_n, \overline{X}_1, \ldots, \overline{X}_n$. If in any disjunction there are lacking both X_i and $\overline{X}_i$, then we can insert the term $(X_i \& \overline{X}_i)$, which is logically false, and again apply the first distributive law, without changing the truth value of the entire sentence. Then each conjunct contains for every i either X_i or $\overline{X}_i$. We need write only one of each group of conjuncts which differ from each other only in the arrangement of the components connected by $\vee$. Thus the expression has assumed the desired form.

In this way every sentence constructed from $X_1, X_2, \ldots, X_n$ is expressible by a *"distinguished"* conjunctive normal form.

This normal form is unique (except for transposition of the conjuncts, and of the disjuncts, among themselves) in the sense that two equivalent combinations of sentences are expressed by the same normal form. For there are exactly $2^{(2^n)}$ different expressions in normal form constructed from X_1, X_2, . . . , X_n, that is, exactly as many as there are different sentences which can be constructed from X_1, X_2, . . . , X_n.

The distinguished normal form allows of the most varied applications. For instance, it may sometimes serve to find a *simpler expression* for a given combination of sentences. For this purpose the given expression is brought into distinguished normal form and then, if need be, simplified by applying the following *rule of elimination*:

$$X\mathfrak{A} \mathbin{\&} \overline{X}\mathfrak{A} \quad \text{eq.} \quad (X \mathbin{\&} \overline{X}) \text{ v } \mathfrak{A} \quad \text{eq.} \quad \mathfrak{A}.$$

As an example let us consider the combination of sentences $A \mathbin{\&} AB$. In order to obtain the development in terms of A and B, let us replace the conjunct A by A v $(B \mathbin{\&} \overline{B})$ and remove the parentheses in accordance with the first distributive law. If the term AB, which appears twice, is written only once, then we have the distinguished normal form:

$$AB \mathbin{\&} A\overline{B}.$$

Factoring out A, we have $A(B \mathbin{\&} \overline{B})$ and, according to the above rule of elimination, A. Thus A is the simplest expression for $A \mathbin{\&} AB$.

Another example is given by the expression $A \mathbin{\&} \overline{A}B$. Here we obtain as the normal form:

$$AB \mathbin{\&} A\overline{B} \mathbin{\&} \overline{A}B.$$

Now the first and second terms and the first and third terms can be combined. To be able to carry out both eliminations, we write the first term twice:

$$(AB \mathbin{\&} A\overline{B}) \mathbin{\&} (AB \mathbin{\&} \overline{A}B).$$

By elimination we have $A \mathbin{\&} B$.

It should be noted further that from the distinguished normal form used above we can determine by inspection whether *a sentence compounded of the elementary sentences* X_1, X_2, . . . , X_n *can be written without the use of the negation sign*. This is the case if and only if the conjunct $\overline{X}_1$ v $\overline{X}_2$ v . . . v $\overline{X}_n$ does not occur in the distinguished normal form of the sentence under consideration. For, a sentence formed from $X_1, X_2, \ldots, X_n$ without negation is true provided true sentences are substituted for $X_1, X_2, \ldots, X_n$. A sentence containing $\overline{X}_1 \vee \overline{X}_2 \vee \ldots \vee \overline{X}_n$ as conjunct does not, however, have this property. Therefore the above-mentioned condition is necessary. On the other hand, it is also sufficient, since each term of the distinguished normal form which is not equal to $\overline{X}_1 \vee \overline{X}_2 \vee \ldots \vee \overline{X}_n$ can be written without negation. For example, we can write

$$X_1 \overline{X}_2 \overline{X}_3 \ldots \overline{X}_n \text{ as } (X_2 \,\&\, X_3 \,\&\, \ldots \,\&\, X_n) \to X_1,$$

$X_1 \overline{X}_2 X_3 \overline{X}_4 X_5 \overline{X}_6 \ldots \text{ as } (X_2 \,\&\, X_4 \,\&\, X_6 \,\&\, \ldots) \to X_1 \vee X_3 \vee X_5 \vee \ldots, \text{ etc.}$

Consequently, exactly half of the $2^{(2^n)}$ sentences which can be constructed from $X_1, X_2, \ldots, X_n$ are expressible without negation.

§ 8. Supplementary Remarks on the Problem of Universal Validity and Satisfiability

The distinguished normal form given above for an expression composed of the elementary sentences $X_1, X_2, \ldots, X_n$ is also called the *development of the expression in terms of* $X_1, X_2, \ldots, X_n$.

Now let there be given a combination of sentences containing, in addition to $X_1, X_2, \ldots, X_n$, also the elementary sentences $Y_1, Y_2, \ldots, Y_m$. In the case of such an expression we can also speak, in a certain sense, of a development in terms of $X_1, \ldots, X_n$. That is, the expression can be rendered as a *conjunction in which each conjunct is the disjunction of one of the constituents of* $X_1, X_2, \ldots, X_n$ *and an expression depending only upon* $Y_1, Y_2, \ldots, Y_m$.

The proof is very simple. We need only develop the expression in terms of all the elementary sentences which occur, *i.e.* $X_1, \ldots, X_n, Y_1, \ldots, Y_m$, and combine those terms which contain the same constituents with regard to $X_1, X_2, \ldots, X_n$.

This development of an expression in terms of $X_1, X_2, \ldots, X_n$ offers certain advantages. We have seen that the decision concerning the *universal validity of an expression, i.e.* the problem of deciding by an effective, finite method whether a given logical expression is logically true or not, is completely solved in the sentential calculus. The solution of this problem is found by transformation into conjunctive normal form. The dual of the problem of universal validity is the problem of *satisfiability*, *i.e.* the problem of deciding whether a given logical expression is logically false, or whether there are sentences which satisfy it, *i.e.* for which it is true. This problem can be solved by transformation into disjunctive normal form, or else by transformation of the negated expression into conjunctive normal form. In connection with these problems of universal validity and satisfiability, certain similar questions may now be considered.

Let there be given an expression in which there occur the elementary sentences $X_1, \ldots, X_n, Y_1, \ldots, Y_m$. Let $Y_1, \ldots, Y_m$ stand for definite fixed sentences. We now ask: What condition must $Y_1, Y_2, \ldots, Y_m$ satisfy in order for the expression to be true for arbitrary choice of the X's? Further: Under what conditions upon $Y_1, Y_2, \ldots, Y_m$ is the expression always false?

In answering these questions, let us assume n equal to 2 for the sake of simplicity. The answer for any n is analogous. Let the development of the expression in terms of X_1 and X_2 be:

$$\text{(A)} \quad \begin{aligned} &\Phi_1(Y_1, \ldots, Y_m) X_1 X_2 \ \& \ \Phi_2(Y_1, \ldots, Y_m) X_1 \overline{X}_2 \ \& \\ &\Phi_3(Y_1, \ldots, Y_m) \overline{X}_1 X_2 \ \& \ \Phi_4(Y_1, \ldots, Y_m) \overline{X}_1 \overline{X}_2. \end{aligned}$$

Here we may assume that all four terms actually occur. If, for example, the term with $X_1\overline{X}_2$ be lacking, we can add an expression $\Phi_2(Y_1, \ldots, Y_m) X_1 \overline{X}_2$ in which $\Phi_2(Y_1, \ldots, Y_m)$ is a logically true sentential combination.

Now we assert: *In order for formula* (A) *to be true for arbitrary* X_1 *and* X_2, *it is necessary and sufficient that the sentence*

$$\begin{aligned} &\Phi_1(Y_1, \ldots, Y_m) \ \& \ \Phi_2(Y_1, \ldots, Y_m) \ \& \\ &\Phi_3(Y_1, \ldots, Y_m) \ \& \ \Phi_4(Y_1, \ldots, Y_m) \end{aligned}$$

be true.

It is clear that the condition is sufficient. Moreover, it is necessary, for if *e.g.* $\Phi_3(Y_1, Y_2, \ldots, Y_m)$ were not true, we could substitute a true sentence for X_1 and a false one for X_2. Then (A) would be equivalent to $\Phi_3(Y_1, \ldots, Y_m)$ and would therefore not be true.

The solution of the dual problem is similar. The expression (A) can be satisfied for some $X_1, \ldots, X_n$ if and only if $Y_1, \ldots, Y_m$ are such that

$$\Phi_1(Y_1, \ldots, Y_m) \vee \Phi_2(Y_1, \ldots, Y_m) \vee$$
$$\Phi_3(Y_1, \ldots, Y_m) \vee \Phi_4(Y_1, \ldots, Y_m)$$

is true.

§ 9. Systematic Survey of All the Deductions from Given Axioms

In § 4 we worked out a method which made it possible for us to find all those combinations of sentences which are true purely for reasons of logic, and to decide in the case of a given combination of sentences whether or not it is of this kind. There now arises the further problem: *From a given set of assumptions* (axioms) *to make all deductions which it is possible to make when the sentences are considered only as unanalyzed wholes.*

Suppose we are given a definite, finite number of axioms, $\mathfrak{A}_1, \mathfrak{A}_2, \ldots, \mathfrak{A}_n$.* The question whether some other definite combination of sentences $\mathfrak{C}$ constitutes a logical consequence of these axioms, can be answered on the basis of what has been developed so far. This is the case if and only if $(\mathfrak{A}_1 \mathbin{\&} \mathfrak{A}_2 \mathbin{\&} \ldots \mathbin{\&} \mathfrak{A}_n) \rightarrow \mathfrak{C}$ is a universally valid logical formula. For example, the deduction of B from A and $A \rightarrow B$, corresponds to the universal validity of the formula

$$(A \mathbin{\&} (A \rightarrow B)) \rightarrow B.$$

However, we have not as yet attained a systematic view of all the possible deductions which can be made. This can be done by using the distinguished conjunctive normal form. Let the elementary sentences which occur in our axioms be $X_1, \ldots, X_n$. Now suppose that all the axioms are connected by &, and suppose that the combination of sentences thus obtained is developed in terms of $X_1, \ldots, X_n$. Then take any constituent (with respect to $X_1, X_2, \ldots, X_n$) which does not appear as a conjunct in this distinguished normal form. By suitable substitution of true or of false sentences for $X_1, \ldots, X_n$, this constituent can be changed into a disjunction of false sentences only, hence into a false sen-

---

* See § 5 for the meaning of German letters.

tence. On the other hand, by means of this substitution our distinguished normal form is transformed into a true sentence. For, each of its conjuncts differs from the constituent under consideration by having in at least one place a disjunct which is the negation of that in the constituent. The constituent considered is therefore not a logical consequence of the axioms. Hence it follows that the distinguished normal form of any consequence of the axioms contains only such constituents as occur also in the development in normal form of the hypothesis (*i.e.* conjunction of axioms).

By applying this observation, we arrive at the following general method for deriving the consequences from a system of axioms:

Connect all the axioms by &, and form the distinguished conjunctive normal form for the resulting expression. Now to obtain in distinguished normal form all the consequences of the axioms, select any of the conjuncts whatsoever of the above distinguished normal form and connect them by &. We can often use the rule of elimination, discussed on page 20, to write these consequences in simpler form.

In the case previously mentioned, where A and $A \rightarrow B$ are taken as axioms, the method yields the following:

A & $(A \rightarrow B)$ is first developed in terms of A and B:

$$A \,\&\, (A \rightarrow B) \quad \text{eq.} \quad A \,\&\, \overline{A}B,$$

$$A \,\&\, \overline{A}B \quad \text{eq.} \quad A\,(B \,\&\, \overline{B}) \,\&\, \overline{A}B,$$

$$A\,(B \,\&\, \overline{B}) \,\&\, \overline{A}B \quad \text{eq.} \quad AB \,\&\, A\overline{B} \,\&\, \overline{A}B.$$

$AB \,\&\, A\overline{B} \,\&\, \overline{A}B$ is the distinguished normal form for the axioms. Thus $AB \,\&\, \overline{A}B$ eq. B is a consequence of the axioms.

The other consequences which can be derived from A and $A \rightarrow B$ are: AB; $A\overline{B}$; $\overline{A}B$; $AB \,\&\, A\overline{B}$ eq. $A\,(B \,\&\, \overline{B})$ eq. A; $A\overline{B} \,\&\, \overline{A}B$ eq. $A \sim B$, and, of course, $AB \,\&\, A\overline{B} \,\&\, \overline{A}B$ eq. $A \,\&\, B$. If one wishes to obtain, in addition, those consequences in which another sentence C appears which does not occur in the axioms, then the hypothesis must be developed in terms of A, B, and C, instead of in terms of A and B.

Another example is the following: Let there be two axioms, $A \sim B$ and $B \sim C$. First, the axioms are written in normal form:

$$\overline{A}B \,\&\, \overline{B}A \,;\; \overline{B}C \,\&\, \overline{C}B.$$

Developing the hypothesis in terms of A, B, and C, we have:

$$AB\overline{C} \,\&\, A\overline{B}C \,\&\, A\overline{B}\overline{C} \,\&\, \overline{A}BC \,\&\, \overline{A}B\overline{C} \,\&\, \overline{A}\,\overline{B}C.$$

For example, one consequence here is:

$$AB\overline{C} \,\&\, A\overline{B}\overline{C} \,\&\, \overline{A}BC \,\&\, \overline{A}\,\overline{B}C.$$

Factoring out:

$$A\overline{C}(B \,\&\, \overline{B}) \,\&\, \overline{A}C(B \,\&\, \overline{B})$$

or

$$A\overline{C} \,\&\, \overline{A}C, \text{ i.e. } A \sim C.$$

We shall give two more examples of this method of obtaining conclusions.

Let A stand for the sentence "Every real number is algebraic," B for the sentence "The set of all real numbers is denumerable." In mathematics the following are shown:

First: $A \to B$, i.e. "If every real number is algebraic, then the set of all real numbers is denumerable."

Second: $\overline{B}$, i.e. "The set of all real numbers is not denumerable."

The hypothesis here is:

$$\overline{A}B \,\&\, \overline{B}$$

or in developed form:

$$\overline{A}B \,\&\, A\overline{B} \,\&\, \overline{A}\,\overline{B}.$$

One of the consequences here is $\overline{A}B \,\&\, \overline{A}\,\overline{B}$ eq. $\overline{A}(B \,\&\, \overline{B})$ eq. $\overline{A}$. I.e., we find: "Not every real number is algebraic." This is the conclusion that there exist transcendental numbers.

As a second example let A, B, and C stand for the following sentences:

A: "The law of vector addition of velocities is valid."

B: "In the system of fixed stars, light travels with the same velocity in all directions."

C: "On the earth light travels with the same velocity in all directions."

Now the following mathematical law holds: $(A \& B) \to \overline{C}$, *i.e.* "If the law of vector addition of velocities is valid, and in the system of fixed stars light travels with the same velocity in all directions, then on the earth light does not travel with the same velocity in all directions."

Further, we gather from physical experience that B and C are true. Thus we have the axioms:

$$(A \& B) \to \overline{C}; \ B; \ C.$$

In its conjunctive normal form the hypothesis is

$$\overline{A}\overline{B}\overline{C} \& B \& C,$$

and in developed form:

$$\overline{A}\overline{B}C \& BA\overline{C} \& BA\overline{C} \& B\overline{A}C \& B\overline{A}\overline{C} \& CA\overline{B} \& C\overline{A}\overline{B}.$$

From this we have the following consequence:

$$\overline{A}\overline{B}\overline{C} \& B\overline{A}\overline{C} \& B\overline{A}C \& \overline{B}\overline{A}C.$$

Factoring out yields:

$$(\overline{B} \& B) \ \overline{A}\overline{C} \& (B \& \overline{B})\overline{A}C,$$

$$\overline{A}\overline{C} \& \overline{A}C,$$

$$(\overline{C} \& C)\overline{A},$$

$$\overline{A}.$$

We have therefore the consequence that the law of vector addition of velocities is not valid.

Any sentence whatsoever can be proved from two mutually contradictory axioms. For if A and $\overline{A}$ are taken as axioms, and if B is any other sentence, the development of the hypothesis $A \& \overline{A}$ in terms of A and B is:

$$AB \& A\overline{B} \& \overline{A}B \& \overline{A}\overline{B},$$

which yields

$$AB \& \overline{A}B,$$

and thus B.

The procedure described above enables us to derive all the consequences which follow from a given set of axioms, or in other words, to find all the sentential combinations which are *weaker* than a given one. Conversely, it may now be asked which sentential combinations are *stronger* than the one given, *i.e.* from which hypotheses it follows as a consequence. We solve this problem in a way similar to the preceding one: First the consequence is developed in terms of all its elementary sentences and thus brought into the distinguished normal form. Next, we select any of the constituents which do not occur, and join them with & to the consequence. In this way all the possible hypotheses are obtained.

§ 10. The Axioms of the Sentential Calculus

The axiomatic form of the theory of the sentential calculus is obtained by making a selection from among the logically true sentential combinations and then giving formal rules in accordance with which all the remaining logically true formulas can be deduced from those selected. These rules play the same role in the logical calculus that logical inference plays in mathematical and physical theories. The fact that logical inference in the usual sense (*i.e.* taking content into account) may not be used here is due to the fact that the very means of logical inference constitute here the object of our investigations.

We make a distinction between *primitive logical formulas* (*axioms*) and *primitive rules for inferring true formulas*. We introduce the following four as primitive logical formulas.

a) $X \vee X \rightarrow X$.

b) $X \rightarrow X \vee Y$.

c) $X \vee Y \rightarrow Y \vee X$.

d) $(X \rightarrow Y) \rightarrow [Z \vee X \rightarrow Z \vee Y]$.

The first axiom means that a sentence is true if the disjunction of that sentence with itself is true. The second axiom is nothing but Rule b2), mentioned on page 14. The third postulates the commutativity of disjunction, and the fourth asserts that in the case of a true implication $X \rightarrow Y$ both sides may be disjunctively connected with any sentence Z whatsoever.

The sign $\rightarrow$, incidentally, will be employed only as an abbreviation. $X \rightarrow Y$ is to be merely a more convenient way of writing

$\overline{X}$ v Y. Thus, *e.g.*, Axiom a), when written without abbreviation, is $\overline{X \text{ v } X}$ v X.

For proving new formulas from the primitive formulas adopted, as well as from formulas already so proved, we have the following two rules:

α) Rule of Substitution

We may substitute for a sentential variable (*i.e.* a capital italic letter) *any given sentential combination, provided that the substitution is made wherever that sentential variable occurs.*

β) Rule of Implication

From the two formulas 𝔄 *and* 𝔄 → 𝔅, *the new formula* 𝔅 *is obtained.*

In the following section we shall explain in detail the manipulation of the two rules for proving new formulas (to be called *theorems*) from established formulas and from the axioms. Before doing this we make some remarks about the axiomatization of the sentential calculus in general.

In setting up the system of axioms, we have employed only the connectives v and $^{-}$ This corresponds to the fact, mentioned above, that these two connectives are sufficient to render all sentential combinations. For the sake of convenience, to be sure, we also use the symbols →, &, and ~. But formulas employing these symbols are to be understood only as abbreviations for formulas which contain only the symbols v and $^{-}$. Thus, a formula 𝔄 → 𝔅 is to be regarded as an abbreviation for $\overline{𝔄}$ v 𝔅; 𝔄 & 𝔅, as an abbreviation for $\overline{\overline{𝔄} \text{ v } \overline{𝔅}}$; and 𝔄 ~ 𝔅, as an abbreviation for (𝔄 → 𝔅) & (𝔅 → 𝔄), *i.e.* for $\overline{\overline{\overline{𝔄} \text{ v } 𝔅} \text{ v } \overline{\overline{𝔅} \text{ v } 𝔄}}$ (cf. the equivalences (21), (28), (24) in § 2).

The system of axioms employed by us is due in essence to Whitehead and Russell (*Principia Mathematica*, first edition). An additional axiom used by them,

$$X \text{ v } (Y \text{ v } Z) \to Y \text{ v } (X \text{ v } Z),$$

which expresses the associativity of the disjunctive connective, proved later to be unnecessary.[1]

---

[1] P. Bernays, *Axiomatische Untersuchung des Aussagenkalküls der Principia Mathematica*. Math. Z. Vol. 25 (1926).

Since the combinations & and $^-$, as well as $\to$ and $^-$, are likewise sufficient to render all sentential combinations, one can also adopt axioms in which only & and $^-$, or only $\to$ and $^-$, appear. In recent years, axiom systems of the latter sort, which employ as primitive only implication and negation, have enjoyed a special interest. The first of these systems of axioms, in which incidentally our Rules a) and β) are also used, goes back as far as Frege.[1] It consists of the following six axioms:

1. $X \to (Y \to X)$,
2. $(X \to (Y \to Z)) \to ((X \to Y) \to (X \to Z))$,
3. $(X \to (Y \to Z)) \to (Y \to (X \to Z))$,
4. $(X \to Y) \to (\overline{Y} \to \overline{X})$,
5. $\overline{\overline{X}} \to X$,
6. $X \to \overline{\overline{X}}$.

As J. Lukasiewicz has shown, this axiom system of Frege's can be replaced by the following simpler system, which consists of only three axioms:

1. $X \to (Y \to X)$,
2. $(X \to (Y \to Z)) \to ((X \to Y) \to (X \to Z))$,
3. $(\overline{X} \to \overline{Y}) \to (Y \to X)$.

It is even possible to adopt as the starting point only a single formula, constructed with implication and negation.[2]

J. Nicod[3] first set forth an axiom system for the sentential calculus which uses only Sheffer's stroke X/Y, mentioned above. This system employs as its single primitive formula

$$[X/(Y/Z)]/\{[U/(U/U)]/[(V/Y)/((X/V)/(X/V))]\}.$$

Instead of our Rule of Implication β), this employs the rule: From the two formulas $\mathfrak{A}$ and $\mathfrak{A}/(\mathfrak{B}/\mathfrak{C})$, the new formula $\mathfrak{C}$ is obtained.

---

[1] G. Frege, *Begriffsschrift, eine der arithmetischen nachgebildete Formelsprache des reinen Denkens.* Halle 1879.

[2] J. Lukasiewicz and A. Tarski, *Untersuchungen über den Aussagenkalkül.* (C. R. Soc. Sci. Varsovie, Vol. 23, Klasse III, Warsaw 1930.)

[3] J. G. P. Nicod, *A reduction in the number of the primitive propositions of logic.* Proc. Camb. Phil. Soc. Vol. 19 (1917). Cf., also, W. V. Quine, *A note on Nicod's postulate,* Mind 41.

Under certain circumstances one will prefer an axiom system of the sentential calculus in which all the fundamental connectives are introduced at the very beginning, namely in case one wishes to exhibit as clearly as possible the role which devolves upon each of these fundamental connectives in logical inference. An axiom system chosen from this point of view has been given by Hilbert and Bernays.[1]

For that matter, another axiomatization of the sentential calculus is contained in our Rules a1) through a4), b1) through b3) (§§ 3 and 4). There we are dealing with a system having the single primitive formula $X \vee \overline{X}$ and six rules of inference.

Finally, we mention, as a system which occupies a special place, the "Calculus of Natural Inferences," set forth by G. Gentzen,[2] which constitutes an attempt to make out of the formal deduction of formulas something more similar to the usual method of proof (taking content into account), such as is customary, *e.g.*, in mathematics. The calculus contains no logical axioms, but only figures of inference which indicate which inferences can be drawn from given assumptions, as well as figures which yield formulas in which the dependence upon the assumptions is eliminated.

§ 11. Examples of the Proof of Theorems from the Axioms

We now return to our system of axioms consisting of the primitive formulas a) through d) and the Rules of Inference α) and β).

We will give a series of examples for the formal proof of theorems from the axioms. We will dwell on this point at some length, since experience shows that the maintenance of the purely formal point of view is especially difficult for the beginner.

In the proof of theorems it is found advisable to embody certain frequently recurring operations in the form of derived

---

[1] D. Hilbert, and P. Bernays; *Grundlagen der Mathematik* I, p. 66.

[2] Gentzen, G.: *Untersuchungen über das logische Schliessen* I and II. Math. Z. Vol. 39 (1934).—Related ideas have been developed independently by Jaskowski. Cf. S. Jaskowski: *On the rules of suppositions in formal logic.* Studia Logica No. 1 (1934).

rules. By such a rule the result of the formal transformation in question will be anticipated once and for all, and the proof of the rule consists in stating the general procedure by which in each individual case the transformation is to be carried out in accordance with the primitive rules.

RULE I. *If* $\mathfrak{A} \vee \mathfrak{A}$ *is a theorem, then the same is true of* $\mathfrak{A}$.

The proof is obtained immediately from Axiom a). By substitution in a) one obtains:

$$\mathfrak{A} \vee \mathfrak{A} \to \mathfrak{A}.$$

Further, since $\mathfrak{A} \vee \mathfrak{A}$ is a theorem, the Rule of Implication furnishes the formula $\mathfrak{A}$.

RULE II. *If* $\mathfrak{A}$ *is a theorem and* $\mathfrak{B}$ *any other formula whatsoever, then* $\mathfrak{A} \vee \mathfrak{B}$ *is also a theorem.*

This rule is obtained from Axiom b) in the same manner as Rule I from a).

In a like manner, Rules III and IV correspond to Axioms c) and d), and, more generally, a corresponding rule is associated with each formula which expresses a relation of implication.

RULE III. *If* $\mathfrak{A} \vee \mathfrak{B}$ *is a theorem, then the same is true of* $\mathfrak{B} \vee \mathfrak{A}$.

RULE IV. *If* $\mathfrak{A} \to \mathfrak{B}$ *is a theorem and* $\mathfrak{C}$ *any other formula whatsoever, then* $\mathfrak{C}\mathfrak{A} \to \mathfrak{C}\mathfrak{B}$ *is also a theorem.*

THEOREM 1.

$$(X \to Y) \to [(Z \to X) \to (Z \to Y)].$$

Proof: $(X \to Y) \to (\bar{Z}X \to \bar{Z}Y)$ is obtained from Axiom d) by substitution of $\bar{Z}$ for Z. This, however, is the same as Theorem 1, if we replace the abbreviation $\to$ by its meaning.

RULE V. *If* $\mathfrak{A} \to \mathfrak{B}$ *and* $\mathfrak{B} \to \mathfrak{C}$ *are theorems, then* $\mathfrak{A} \to \mathfrak{C}$ *is also a theorem.*

This rule corresponds to Theorem 1. We prove it by substituting in Theorem 1 $\mathfrak{B}$, $\mathfrak{C}$, and $\mathfrak{A}$ for X, Y, and Z respectively, and then applying the Rule of Implication twice.

THEOREM 2. $\overline{X} \vee X$.

Proof :

$$X \to X \vee X \qquad \text{[by substitution}$$
$$\text{of } X \text{ for } Y \text{ in b)]},$$
$$X \vee X \to X \qquad \text{[by a)]},$$
$$X \to X \qquad \text{[by Rule V]}.$$

The last formula is an abbreviated way of writing $\overline{X} \vee X$.

THEOREM 3. $X \vee \overline{X}$.

This theorem is obtained from Theorem 2 by the application of Rule III.

THEOREM 4. $X \to \overline{\overline{X}}$.

Proof : Theorem 4 is an abbreviation for $\overline{X}\overline{X}$, and this formula results from Theorem 3 by substituting $\overline{X}$ for X.

THEOREM 5. $\overline{\overline{X}} \to X$.

Proof :

$$\overline{X} \to \overline{\overline{\overline{X}}} \qquad \text{[by substitution}$$
$$\text{in Theorem 4]},$$
$$X\overline{X} \to X\overline{\overline{\overline{X}}} \qquad \text{[by Rule IV]},$$
$$X\overline{\overline{\overline{X}}} \qquad \text{[because of Theorem 3}$$
$$\text{and Rule } \beta)],$$
$$\overline{\overline{\overline{X}}}X \qquad \text{[by Rule III]}.$$

The last formula is Theorem 5.

THEOREM 6. $(X \to Y) \to (\overline{Y} \to \overline{X})$.

Proof :

$$Y \to \overline{\overline{Y}} \qquad \text{[Theorem 4]},$$
$$\overline{X}Y \to \overline{X}\overline{\overline{Y}} \qquad \text{[Rule IV]},$$
$$\overline{X}\overline{\overline{Y}} \to \overline{\overline{Y}}\overline{X} \qquad \text{[Substitution in c)]},$$
$$\overline{X}Y \to \overline{\overline{Y}}\overline{X} \qquad \text{[Rule V]}.$$

This is the desired theorem.

RULE VI. *If an expression* 𝔄 *occurs as a part of a sentential combination, a combination which will be represented in this connection by* $\Phi(\mathfrak{A})$, *and if* 𝔄 → 𝔅 *and* 𝔅 → 𝔄 *are theorems, then* $\Phi(\mathfrak{A}) \to \Phi(\mathfrak{B})$ *and* $\Phi(\mathfrak{B}) \to \Phi(\mathfrak{A})$ *are also theorems.* The form of 𝔄 and the entire expression do not, incidentally, determine uniquely the meaning of $\Phi(\mathfrak{A})$. The expression $X \to XY$, for example, may be represented in three different senses as $\Phi(X)$, since each of the three expressions $\mathfrak{A} \to XY$, $X \to \mathfrak{A}Y$, or $\mathfrak{A} \to \mathfrak{A}Y$ may be taken for $\Phi(\mathfrak{A})$. Rule VI holds for each of the possible definitions of $\Phi(\mathfrak{A})$.

This rule may also be stated thus: *Two expressions which stand in a relation of mutual implication may in any theorem be substituted for each other.*

Proof: It is sufficient to prove the rule for the case in which 𝔄 appears only once in $\Phi(\mathfrak{A})$, and in which $\Phi(\mathfrak{A})$ has one of the forms $\overline{\mathfrak{A}}$, ℭ𝔄, and 𝔄ℭ. The general rule is secured through multiple applications of this simple rule by, so to speak, building up Φ from within. For one obtains, successively, for each partial expression Φ' of Φ:

$$\Phi'(\mathfrak{B}) \to \Phi'(\mathfrak{A}) \text{ and } \Phi'(\mathfrak{A}) \to \Phi'(\mathfrak{B}).$$

Thus, let 𝔄 → 𝔅 and 𝔅 → 𝔄 be already proved. Then we shall prove:

α) $\overline{\mathfrak{A}} \to \overline{\mathfrak{B}}$ and $\overline{\mathfrak{B}} \to \overline{\mathfrak{A}}$.

Both these formulas are obtained by first proving

$$(\mathfrak{A} \to \mathfrak{B}) \to (\overline{\mathfrak{B}} \to \overline{\mathfrak{A}})$$

and

$$(\mathfrak{B} \to \mathfrak{A}) \to (\overline{\mathfrak{A}} \to \overline{\mathfrak{B}}),$$

by substitution in Theorem 6, and then using the fact that 𝔄 → 𝔅 and 𝔅 → 𝔄 are already proved.

β) ℭ𝔄 → ℭ𝔅; ℭ𝔅 → ℭ𝔄.

These formulas are obtained from 𝔄 → 𝔅 and 𝔅 → 𝔄, respectively, by application of Rule IV.

γ) 𝔄ℭ → 𝔅ℭ; 𝔅ℭ → 𝔄ℭ.

This case may be reduced to β), if one applies Axiom c) and Rule V several times.

As an application of Rule VI and Axiom c) the *commutativity of disjunction* is obtained. For,

$$\mathfrak{A} \vee \mathfrak{B} \rightarrow \mathfrak{B} \vee \mathfrak{A} \text{ and } \mathfrak{B} \vee \mathfrak{A} \rightarrow \mathfrak{A} \vee \mathfrak{B}$$

are obtained by substituting in c) ; hence in any sentential combination, the disjunction $\mathfrak{B} \vee \mathfrak{A}$ may always be substituted for the disjunction $\mathfrak{A} \vee \mathfrak{B}$.

In a similar manner, it follows from Theorems 4 and 5 and Rule VI that $\overline{\overline{\mathfrak{A}}}$ may be substituted for $\mathfrak{A}$, and conversely.

THEOREM 7. $X \& Y \rightarrow \overline{X} \vee \overline{Y}$.

Proof: $X \& Y$ is an abbreviation for $\overline{\overline{X}\,\overline{Y}}$. The formula $\overline{\overline{\overline{X}\,\overline{Y}}} \rightarrow \overline{X}\,\overline{Y}$ is obtained from $\overline{\overline{X}} \rightarrow X$ by substitution.

Likewise the following theorems are secured from $X \rightarrow \overline{\overline{X}}$:

THEOREM 8. $\overline{X} \vee \overline{Y} \rightarrow \overline{X \& Y}$.

THEOREM 9. $\overline{X \vee Y} \rightarrow \overline{X} \& \overline{Y}$.

THEOREM 10. $\overline{X} \& \overline{Y} \rightarrow \overline{X \vee Y}$.

Proof: If no abbreviation is used, Theorems 9 and 10 read:

$$\overline{X \vee Y} \rightarrow \overline{\overline{\overline{X}} \vee \overline{\overline{Y}}} \text{ and } \overline{\overline{\overline{X}} \vee \overline{\overline{Y}}} \rightarrow \overline{X \vee Y}.$$

They follow from $\overline{X \vee Y} \rightarrow \overline{X \vee Y}$, when $\overline{\overline{X}}$ is substituted for X and $\overline{\overline{Y}}$ for Y on the right and left respectively in accordance with Rule VI.

Theorems 7 and 8 and Theorems 9 and 10, together with Rule VI, furnish us the earlier Rule a3), p. 12.

The following is a further application of Rule VI: Since $X \vee X \rightarrow X$ holds by Axiom a), and since $X \rightarrow X \vee X$ is obtained from Axiom b) by substitution, an expression of the form $\mathfrak{A} \vee \mathfrak{A}$ may always be replaced by $\mathfrak{A}$, and conversely.

THEOREM 11. $X \& Y \rightarrow Y \& X$.

Proof: $\overline{\overline{X}\,\overline{Y}} \rightarrow \overline{\overline{Y}\,\overline{X}}$ is obtained from $\overline{\overline{X}\,\overline{Y}} \rightarrow \overline{\overline{X}\,\overline{Y}}$ by applying the commutative law of disjunction.

THEOREM 12. $X \& Y \to X$.
Proof:

$$\overline{X} \to \overline{X}\overline{Y} \qquad \text{[by Axiom b)]},$$
$$\overline{\overline{X}\overline{Y}} \to \overline{\overline{X}} \qquad \text{[by Theorem 6]},$$
$$X \& Y \to \overline{\overline{X}},$$
$$X \& Y \to X.$$

THEOREM 13. $X \& Y \to Y$.
The proof follows from Theorems 11 and 12.

THEOREM 14. $X(YZ) \to Y(XZ)$.
Proof:

$$Z \to XZ \qquad \text{[from Axiom b) by transposing the disjuncts]},$$
$$YZ \to Y(XZ) \qquad \text{[Rule IV]},$$
$$X(YZ) \to X(Y(XZ)) \qquad \text{[Rule IV]},$$
$$X(YZ) \to (Y(XZ))X^* \qquad \text{[commutativity of disjunction]},$$
$$X \to ZX \qquad \text{[from Axiom b) by transposing the disjuncts]},$$
$$XZ \to Y(XZ) \qquad \text{[substitution in above formula]},$$
$$X \to Y(XZ) \qquad \text{[Rule V]},$$
$$(Y(XZ))X \to (Y(XZ))(Y(XZ)) \qquad \text{[Rule IV]},$$
$$(Y(XZ))X \to Y(XZ).^{**} \qquad \text{[replacement of } \mathfrak{A} \text{ v } \mathfrak{A} \text{ by } \mathfrak{A}.]$$

According to Rule V, * and ** give:
$$X(YZ) \to Y(XZ).$$

THEOREM 15. $X(YZ) \to (XY)Z$.
Proof:

$$X(YZ) \to X(ZY) \qquad \text{[commutative law]},$$
$$X(ZY) \to Z(XY) \qquad \text{[Theorem 14]},$$
$$X(YZ) \to Z(XY) \qquad \text{[Rule V]}.$$

Theorem 15 is obtained from this by applying the commutative law.

THEOREM 16. $(XY)Z \to X(YZ)$.

Proof:

$$Z(YX) \to (ZY)X \qquad \text{[substitution in Theorem 15]}.$$

By using the commutative law, $Z(YX)$ can be replaced by $(XY)Z$ and $(ZY)X$ by $X(YZ)$.

From Theorems 15 and 16 and Rule VI it follows that not only the order but also the parenthesizing of disjuncts is immaterial. Thus we have proved also the *associative law* for disjunction.

THEOREM 17. $X \& (Y \& Z) \to (X \& Y) \& Z$,

$$(X \& Y) \& Z \to X \& (Y \& Z).$$

Proof: $X \& (Y \& Z)$ is an abbreviation for $\overline{\overline{X}\overline{Y}\overline{Z}}$, $(X \& Y) \& Z$ is an abbreviation for $\overline{\overline{X}\overline{Y}\overline{Z}}$. These two expressions, however, are equivalent according to our preceding rules, and may be substituted for each other at will.

THEOREM 18. $X \to (Y \to X \& Y)$.

Proof:

$$(\overline{X}\overline{Y}) \, \overline{X}\overline{Y} \qquad \text{[substitution in Theorem 3]}.$$

$\overline{X}(\overline{Y}\overline{X}\overline{Y})$ is obtained from this by parenthesizing the disjuncts differently. This is the desired theorem.

RULE VII. $\mathfrak{B} \to (\mathfrak{A} \to \mathfrak{C})$ *and* $(\mathfrak{A} \& \mathfrak{B}) \to \mathfrak{C}$ *may be substituted for* $\mathfrak{A} \to (\mathfrak{B} \to \mathfrak{C})$.

The proof is obtained at once from our rules if the abbreviations $\to$ and $\&$ are replaced by their meaning.

RULE VIII. $\mathfrak{A} \to \mathfrak{B}$ *may be substituted for* $\mathfrak{A} \to (\mathfrak{A} \to \mathfrak{B})$.

Proof: $(\overline{\mathfrak{A}\mathfrak{A}})\mathfrak{B}$ or $\overline{\mathfrak{A}\mathfrak{B}}$ may be substituted for $\overline{\mathfrak{A}(\overline{\mathfrak{A}\mathfrak{B}})}$.

THEOREM 19. $X(Y \& Z) \rightarrow XY \& XZ$.

Proof:

$$Y \& Z \rightarrow Y \qquad \text{[Theorem 12]},$$

$$X(Y \& Z) \rightarrow XY \qquad \text{[by Rule IV]}.$$

Likewise one obtains from Theorem 13:

$$X(Y \& Z) \rightarrow XZ,$$

$$XY \rightarrow (XZ \rightarrow XY \& XZ) \qquad \text{[Theorem 18]},$$

$$X(Y \& Z) \rightarrow (XZ \rightarrow XY \& XZ) \qquad \text{[by Rule V]},$$

$$XZ \rightarrow \big(X(Y \& Z) \rightarrow XY \& XZ\big) \qquad \text{[by Rule VII]},$$

$$X(Y \& Z) \rightarrow \big(X(Y \& Z) \rightarrow XY \& XZ\big) \qquad \text{[by Rule V]},$$

$$X(Y \& Z) \rightarrow XY \& XZ \qquad \text{[Rule VIII]}.$$

THEOREM 20. $XY \& XZ \rightarrow X(Y \& Z)$.

Proof:

$$Y \rightarrow (Z \rightarrow Y \& Z) \qquad \text{[Theorem 18]},$$

$$(Z \rightarrow Y \& Z) \rightarrow \big(XZ \rightarrow X(Y \& Z)\big) \qquad \text{[Axiom d)]},$$

$$Y \rightarrow \big(XZ \rightarrow X(Y \& Z)\big) \qquad \text{[Rule V]},$$

$$XZ \rightarrow \big(Y \rightarrow X(Y \& Z)\big) \qquad \text{[Rule VII]},$$

$$\big(Y \rightarrow X(Y \& Z)\big) \rightarrow [XY \rightarrow X(X(Y \& Z))] \qquad \text{[substitution in Axiom d)]},$$

$$XZ \rightarrow [XY \rightarrow X(X(Y \& Z))] \qquad \text{[Rule V]};$$

for $X(X(Y \& Z))$ we may substitute $(XX)(Y \& Z)$ and then $X(Y \& Z)$.

$$XZ \rightarrow \big(XY \rightarrow X(Y \& Z)\big).$$

From this we obtain the above theorem by Rule VII.

Theorems 19 and 20, together with Rule VI, yield the proof of the distributive law.

Further proofs of theorems and rules turn out to be unnecessary. For we have seen that Rules a1) through a4) and b1) through b3), which were previously presented, may be obtained from the axioms as derived rules. Hence it follows that all the observations which we made earlier in connection with these rules, *e.g.* those which are concerned with the principle of duality and with the normal form, may also be derived from the axioms. Therefore, it is not necessary to go back each time as far as the axioms in order to show the provability of a formula. For, a sentential formula is provable from the axioms if and only if each disjunction of its conjunctive normal form contains two components of which one is the negation of the other.

§ 12. The Consistency of the System of Axioms

The axiomatic treatment of the sentential calculus makes it possible to ask the questions and introduce the considerations which are peculiar to the axiomatic method. The most important of the questions which arise are those concerning the *consistency*, *independence*, and *completeness* of the system of axioms. We shall consider first the consistency of the axioms.

The question of consistency may here be posed in an appropriate form. We shall call the axioms consistent if it is impossible to prove, by means of the calculus, two sentential combinations which are mutually contradictory, *i.e.* which result from the pair of sentences $X, \overline{X}$, if the same substitution for X is made in both.

This definition of consistency requires an explanation. It might seem as though we were giving a preferred position to one particular logical principle—the principle of contradiction. The fact is, however, that the occurrence of a formal contradiction, *i.e.* the provability of two formulas $\mathfrak{A}$ and $\overline{\mathfrak{A}}$, would condemn the entire calculus as meaningless; for we have observed above that if two sentences of form $\mathfrak{A}$ and $\overline{\mathfrak{A}}$ were provable, the same would be true of any other sentences whatsoever. Thus consistency of the calculus in the sense of the definition has the same meaning as the stipulation that not every arbitrary formula be provable.

In order to prove the consistency of the calculus, we proceed as follows.

We interpret the sentential symbols X, Y, Z, . . . as arithmetical variables which assume only the values 0 and 1. Further, we interpret X v Y as the arithmetical product, and so define $\overline{X}$

that $\overline{0}$ shall equal 1 and $\overline{1}$ shall equal 0. On the basis of this interpretation, every sentential combination represents an arithmetical function of the elementary sentences which assumes only the values 0 and 1. If this function is identically 0, then for the sake of brevity we will also speak of the symbolic expression as being identically 0.

On the basis of this interpretation, we may now state a common property of all the formulas provable from our axioms. This consists in the fact that, on the basis of the arithmetical interpretation, the formulas yield the value 0 for every possible set of values of the variables, *i.e.* they are identically equal to 0.

That the Axioms a) through d) possess this property, is shown thus:

We establish by testing that $\overline{X} \vee X$ always has the value 0. From this it follows that $\overline{X \vee X} \vee X$ [Axiom a)] always equals 0, because $X \vee X$ always has the same value as X. Further, $\overline{X}(XY)$ [Axiom b)] always has the same value as $(\overline{X} \vee X) Y$, because the arithmetical product is associative. Accordingly, it is always 0, because $0 \vee Y$ is always equal to 0. Since $Y \vee X$ always has the same value as $X \vee Y$, the expression $\overline{X \vee Y} \vee (Y \vee X)$, as a special case of $\overline{X}X$, is always equal to 0. Hence Axiom c) always yields the value 0. Finally, this is also true for Axiom d) ; for if Z is 0, then one factor is 0, and if Z is 1, $Z \vee X$ has the same value as X, and $Z \vee Y$ the same value as Y, so that the entire formula gives the same value as $\overline{\overline{XY}\overline{X}Y}$, again a special case of $\overline{X}X$.

Thus the formulas of the four axioms indeed have the above-mentioned property. Now under application of the two rules used for inferring new formulas, namely, the Rule of Substitution and the Rule of Implication, the property persists. For, with regard to the first rule, it is evident that the range of values for the variables can certainly not be extended by substituting an expression for any of them. And when we infer formula 𝔅 from the two formulas 𝔄 and $\overline{\mathfrak{A}}\mathfrak{B}$ by means of the second rule, the property of always yielding the value 0 is carried over from the last two formulas to the one inferred. For, since the formula 𝔄 always yields the value 0, $\overline{\mathfrak{A}}$ always has the value 1 ; hence $\overline{\mathfrak{A}}\mathfrak{B}$ always has the same value as $\mathfrak{B}$, so that $\mathfrak{B}$, as well as $\overline{\mathfrak{A}\mathfrak{B}}$, always has the value 0.

Thus we see that our calculus indeed gives only such formulas as always yield the value 0 in the arithmetical interpretation. But with this statement, we really have completed the proof. For obviously, two formulas which arise from X and $\overline{X}$ by substituting for X both times the same sentential combination cannot both possess the property of always yielding 0. Rather, if one formula always has the value 0, then the other always has the value 1.

§ 13.   The Independence and Completeness of the System

After the question of consistency, which we have been able to answer affirmatively for the axiom system, comes the further question whether the axioms are all *independent* of one another, or whether we may not dispense with one or another of them.[1]

The answer is that the axiom system does satisfy the requirement of independence.

We first show that Axiom a) $\overline{X \vee X} \vee X$ cannot be proved from the other axioms, and indeed not even if the formula $\overline{X} \vee X$ should be added as an axiom, so that the formula a) cannot be replaced in the system of axioms by the simpler $\overline{X}X$. For the other axioms also, the proof of independence will be carried out in the stricter sense that the axiom concerned can not be replaced by $\overline{X} \vee X$.

Again we prove this by means of an arithmetical interpretation. As values for the variables $X, Y, Z, \dots$, take the residues 0, 1, and 2 modulo 4. The sign "v" is again to represent ordinary multiplication, and $\overline{X}$ is defined thus: $\overline{0}$ signifies 1, $\overline{1}$ signifies 0, $\overline{2}$ signifies 2.

We can now verify that $\overline{X} \vee X$ and the Axioms b), c), and d), with this interpretation of the variables, *always* yield the residue 0, and that this property is transferred, in applying the two

---

[1] This question about the independence of the axiom system is also solved in the work of P. Bernays, referred to on p. 28, *Axiomatische Untersuchung*, etc.

rules, to all of the formulas deduced from these four. The proof
of this is similar to the above proof of consistency. If, therefore,
Axiom a) were deducible by means of the rules from b), c), d),
and $\overline{X} \vee X$, it would necessarily follow that $\overline{XX} \vee X$ yields the
residue 0 for every admissible value of X. This, however, is not
the case. For, if we substitute for X the value 2, then we obtain:

$$\overline{2 \vee 2} \vee 2 = \overline{0} \vee 2 = 1 \vee 2 = 2,$$

and thus not the value 0.

We can show the independence of Axiom b) $\overline{X} \vee (X \vee Y)$ from
the rest of the axioms (including $\overline{X} \vee X$) thus: Once more X, Y,
and Z are to be regarded as arithmetical variables, in this case
having the range of values 0, 1, 2, 3. Now, however, we define the
sign "v" for these variables by

$$0 \vee 0 = 0 \vee 1 = 0 \vee 2 = 0 \vee 3 = 0; \quad 1 \vee 1 = 1 \vee 2 = 1 \vee 3 = 1 ;$$

$$2 \vee 2 = 2; \quad 3 \vee 3 = 3; \quad 2 \vee 3 = 2,$$

and by positing that the commutative law is valid. Further, by
$\overline{0}$, $\overline{1}$, $\overline{2}$, and $\overline{3}$, we shall mean 1, 0, 3, and 2, respectively. Whatever
values we choose for the variables, Axioms a), c), d) and $\overline{X} \vee X$
always give the value 0 or 2. This property persists for all formulas which are provable from a), c), d), and $\overline{X} \vee X$ by means
of the two rules. On the other hand, $\overline{X}(XY)$ has the value 1 if
we take $X = 2$ and $Y = 1$.

We show the independence of Axiom c) $\overline{XY}(YX)$ similarly.
$\overline{0}$ is defined as 1, $\overline{1}$ as 0, $\overline{2}$ as 0, $\overline{3}$ as 2. Further, let

$$0 \vee 0 = 0 \vee 1 = 0 \vee 2 = 0 \vee 3 = 1 \vee 0 = 2 \vee 0 = 3 \vee 0 = 0;$$

$$1 \vee 1 = 1; \quad 1 \vee 2 = 2 \vee 1 = 2; \quad 1 \vee 3 = 3 \vee 1 = 3;$$

$$2 \vee 3 = 0; \quad 3 \vee 2 = 3; \quad 2 \vee 2 = 2; \quad 3 \vee 3 = 3.$$

We easily see that Axioms a), b), d), and $\overline{X} \vee X$ yield the
value 0 when the numbers 0, 1, 2, and 3, are substituted in any
arbitrary manner for the capital italic letters, and that this property persists in the proof of new formulas. On the other hand,
c) has the value 3 if 2 is substituted for X and 3 for Y. This

proof of independence gives us even more. It shows that the associative law

$$\overline{X(YZ)}\,((XY)Z)$$

cannot be proved without the use of Axiom c). For if in this formula we substitute 3 for X, 2 for Y, and 3 for Z, then we have

$$\overline{3 \text{ v } (2 \text{ v } 3)} \text{ v } \big((3 \text{ v } 2) \text{ v } 3\big) = \overline{0} \text{ v } 3 = 1 \text{ v } 3 = 3.$$

The associative law is therefore independent of Axioms a), b), and d).

There yet remains the task of showing the independence of Axiom d) from the rest of the axioms. This may be accomplished by the following system of definitions:

Let X, Y, and Z be variables which can assume the values 0, 1, 2, and 3.

Let

$$\overline{0} = 1\,,\ \ \overline{1} = 0\,,\ \ \overline{2} = 3,\ \ \overline{3} = 0.$$

$$0 \text{ v } 0 = 0 \text{ v } 1 = 1 \text{ v } 0 = 0 \text{ v } 2 = 2 \text{ v } 0 =$$
$$0 \text{ v } 3 = 3 \text{ v } 0 = 2 \text{ v } 3 = 3 \text{ v } 2 = 0.$$

$$1 \text{ v } 1 = 1,\ \ 1 \text{ v } 2 = 2 \text{ v } 1 = 2,\ \ 1 \text{ v } 3 = 3 \text{ v } 1 = 3.$$
$$2 \text{ v } 2 = 2,\ \ 3 \text{ v } 3 = 3.$$

Then the Axioms a), b), c), and $\overline{X} \text{ v } X$, as well as all formulas proved from them, always give the value 0. On the other hand, d) has the value 2 if one sets $X = 3$, $Y = 1$, and $Z = 2$.

We have thus shown the *independence of Axioms* a) *through* d). Let us now consider the question of *completeness*. The completeness of an axiom system may be defined in two ways. First, it may be taken to mean that all the true formulas of a certain domain which is characterized by content can be proved from the set of axioms. However, the concept of completeness may also be more strictly formulated, so that an axiom system is termed complete only if a contradiction always arises when there is added to the axioms a formula not previously provable from them.

Completeness in the first sense would here assert that all the logically true sentential formulas are provable from Axioms a) through d). This requirement, as we have already seen, is satisfied.

But the system is also complete in the stricter sense. We can convince ourselves of this in the following manner: Let $\mathfrak{A}$ be any formula which is not provable from the axioms. Let $\mathfrak{B}$ be the expression in conjunctive normal form belonging to $\mathfrak{A}$. Since $\mathfrak{B}$ is no more a provable formula than $\mathfrak{A}$ is, a disjunction $\mathfrak{C}$ containing no mutually contradictory components must occur among the conjuncts of $\mathfrak{B}$.

If in $\mathfrak{C}$ we put X for every un-negated sentential symbol and $\overline{X}$ for every negated sentential symbol, then we obtain a disjunction of the form $X \vee X \vee X \vee \ldots \vee X$, which, according to the rules of the sentential calculus, is equivalent to X. If now $\mathfrak{A}$ should be postulated as a true formula, then $\mathfrak{B}$ and $\mathfrak{C}$ also, and finally X, would be obtained as true formulas. But then we could also substitute $\overline{X}$ for X and thereby get a contradiction. Thus the axiom system under consideration turns out to be complete.

CHAPTER II

THE CALCULUS OF CLASSES
(MONADIC PREDICATE CALCULUS)

So far, the form of our logical calculus is adequate for the precise rendering of those logical connections in which the sentences appear as unanalyzed wholes. For the purposes of logic in general, however, there is no question but that the sentential calculus is inadequate. We cannot even obtain from it conclusions of the simple kind which are referred to in traditional logic by the catch-words "Barbara," "Celarent," "Darii," etc. For example, it would be in vain to search for the formal rendering of the logical relation expressed in the following three sentences:

> "All men are mortal;
> Socrates is a man;
> therefore, Socrates is mortal."

The reason for this is that inferences of this sort depend not only upon the sentences as wholes, but also upon the inner logical structure of the sentences which is expressed gramatically by the relation between subject and predicate and which plays an essential role. Because of these considerations, we are led to alter the calculus, or at least its interpretation as regards content.

§ 1. Reinterpretation of the Symbolism of the Sentential Calculus

In the following calculus we shall use the same logical symbols as in the sentential calculus. By X, Y, Z, . . . we shall now, however, no longer understand entire sentences but predicates. For example, X can stand for the predicate "is mortal" or "is divisible" or "has a cause." Here the use of the term "predicate" is the one usual in philosophy, namely, that by which *one* subject can be more particularly characterized. In the course of this book

44

(*viz.* in the third and fourth chapters), however, the term "predicate" will be used in another, wider sense, into which we need not enter here. There we will be concerned with predicates having several subjects. Therefore we will call predicates in the ordinary sense, which are the only ones dealt with in this chapter, more precisely monadic predicates; but in the following we will, for the most part, omit the adjective "monadic."

If X is any predicate, *e.g.*, "is pretty," then $\overline{X}$ is to stand for the contradictory predicate "is not pretty." If X and Y respectively stand for the predicates "is mortal" and "is rational," then $X \,\&\, Y$ is the symbol for the predicate "is mortal and is rational," and $X \vee Y$ is the symbol for "is mortal or is rational." The other logical signs may once more be used as abbreviations.

Predicates considered by themselves are neither true nor false. Hence, to say that a formula such as X or $X \vee Y$ is true must now have another sense than hitherto. We shall understand it to mean that the predicate X or $X \vee Y$ holds for *all* objects.

In this manner the interpretations for all symbols in the monadic predicate calculus are fixed. All the formulas will have the meaning of *universal judgments*. In order to represent an ordinary universal judgment, as for instance "All men are mortal," such a judgment may first be put in the form: "All objects are not men or are mortal." If the symbol X is introduced for the predicate "is a man" and Y for the predicate "is mortal," then the symbolic representation of the judgment is given by $\overline{X} \vee Y$. Correspondingly, a universal negative judgment, such as "No man is perfect," may be represented by the formula $\overline{X} \vee \overline{Y}$, in which X and Y respectively stand for the predicates "is a man," and "is perfect." The exact interpretation of the formula $\overline{X} \vee \overline{Y}$ is as follows: All objects are not men or are not perfect.

At this point we may again inquire about those formulas which are logically true; *i.e.*, about those formulas from which we obtain by substitution of arbitrary predicates for the variables $X, Y, \ldots$ a predicate which holds for all objects. It is then easy to see that *in this new interpretation of the calculus, the system of logically true formulas is exactly the same as in the sentential calculus*.

For in the first place the equivalences a1) through a4), which make possible the transformation of expressions into conjunctive normal form, are valid. Further, it is clear that a formula in normal form is logically true if and only if each conjunct contains a disjunction $X \vee \overline{X}$. We can therefore retain all of the formalism of the sentential calculus. We need only give the formulas another interpretation.

In addition to the original interpretation and the interpretation in the sense of the predicate calculus, there is yet a *third interpretation* for the formulas of the sentential calculus. However, this, in contradistinction to the predicate calculus, does not introduce new logical relations, but merely gives a different representation of the facts which are expressible in the predicate calculus, the new representation having the advantage of being more intuitive. This alteration in the representation consists in characterizing the predicates by their *extension* instead of according to their *content*. To each predicate corresponds a certain "class"[1] of objects, consisting of all objects for which the predicate holds. The case of a class containing no object is of course not excluded here. Classes are now to be taken as the entities dealt with by the calculus, which in this interpretation will be called the *calculus of classes*.

$\overline{X}$ represents the class consisting of all objects which do not belong to the class X. $X \& Y$ represents the intersection of the two classes X and Y, and $X \vee Y$, their union. $X \to Y$ and $X \sim Y$ can be employed, as before, as abbreviations for $\overline{X} \vee Y$ and $\overline{X} \vee Y$ & $\overline{Y} \vee X$, respectively. To say that a formula X is true, will mean that the class X is that which consists of all objects. With these conventions for the class calculus, all the rules of the predicate calculus are valid without alteration. The truth of $X \to Y$ means, according to this interpretation, that the class which corresponds to X is a sub-class of the class Y. The formula $X \sim Y$ is true if and only if the classes X and Y are identical.

The universal judgment "All men are mortal" may be formulated in the class calculus thus:

---

[1] In mathematics the term "set" is used rather than "class."

"The union of the class of not-men and the class of mortals comprises all things."

The formal representation is the same as in the predicate calculus.

§ 2. The Combination of the Calculus of Classes with the Sentential Calculus

The predicate calculus is not itself sufficient to formalize all the inferences of traditional logic, because a means of representing *particular judgments* is lacking. *This representation is obtained only by uniting the sentential calculus with the predicate or class calculus.* We arrive at this unification on the basis of the consideration that the relations of the predicate calculus constitute sentences which can be subjected to the rules of the sentential calculus. This idea leads to the construction of a *combined calculus,* in which the logical connectives &, v, and $^{-}$ are used sometimes for combining sentences and sometimes for combining predicates.

But it would then offhand be doubtful whether a sentence $\bar{X}$ signifies that the predicate X holds for no object or whether it signifies that it is not true that X holds for all objects. For example, if X stands for the predicate "to be pretty," then according to the one interpretation, $\bar{X}$ would read "All things are not-pretty," and according to the other interpretation, "Not all things are pretty." This difficulty may be avoided by enclosing the predicate within two vertical lines. $|\ X \text{ v } Y\ |$ would then mean that the predicate X v Y holds for all objects. On the other hand, $|\ X\ |\text{ v }|\ Y\ |$ would mean that the predicate X holds for all objects or the predicate Y holds for all objects. The two sentences which just before led to confusion are now differentiated by $|\ \bar{X}\ |$ and $\overline{|\ X\ |}$. By means of the combined calculus, we now can render *particular sentences.* For example, the sentence "Some numbers are odd" may be transformed into "It is not true that all numbers are even." For, let X stand for the predicate "to be a number," Y for the predicate "to be even." The sentence "All numbers are even" is symbolized by $|\ \bar{X} \text{ v } Y\ |$. Hence the contradictory of this sentence is rendered by $\overline{|\ \bar{X} \text{ v } Y\ |}$. In general, $\overline{|\ \bar{X} \text{ v } Y\ |}$ stands for the sentence "There are things for which X and $\overline{Y}$ hold at the same time."

In the combined calculus a series of new logically true formulas is added to the previous ones. Some of these, for example, are:

$$[\mid X \to Y \mid \& \mid Y \to Z \mid] \to \mid X \to Z \mid ,$$
$$\mid X \mid \& \mid Y \mid \sim \mid X \& Y \mid.$$

A systematic construction and discussion of these formulas is not given, for reasons mentioned at the end of the next section.

§ 3. Systematic Derivation of the Traditional Aristotelian Inferences

Having sufficiently supplemented our calculus, we turn now to its application to the theory of logical inferences. The task is to determine how the classical Aristotelian syllogisms (figures of inference) are to be included in our combined calculus and how we are to systematize and derive them within the framework of this calculus.

The characteristic properties of the inferences to be considered are the following: They consist of three sentences, of which the third (the conclusion) is a logical consequence of the first two (the premises). Each of the three sentences has one of the following four forms:

"All A is B" (universal affirmative judgment).

"Some A is B" (particular affirmative judgment).

"No A is B" (universal negative judgment).

"Some A is not B" (particular negative judgment).

It is customary to use the vowels A, I, E, O (in the given order) as an abbreviated notation for these four forms. Let the symbol AB serve as a common symbol for the four kinds of judgment.

In the three sentences there occur altogether three terms, namely, the *subject* (S), the *predicate* (P), and the *middle term* (M). The conclusion has the form SP. The first premise contains the terms M and P; the second, the terms M and S. Consequently, there result the following four figures of syllogistic inference:[1]

MP	PM	MP	PM
SM	SM	MS	MS
$\overline{SP}$	$\overline{SP}$	$\overline{SP}$	$\overline{SP}$

Since there are four possible forms of judgment A, I, E, O to which each one of the three sentences of each of these four figures could belong, there would be 256 different kinds of syllogisms possible on purely combinatorial grounds. The number of possibilities is materially reduced, however, by the requirement that the conclusion must follow from the premises. Aristotelian logic shows that 19 different syllogisms are admissible. Three-syllable mnemonic words have been introduced for these, in which the vowels in order indicate the forms of judgment to which the three sentences of the syllogism belong. With this terminology, we obtain the following table:

First Figure	Second Figure	Third Figure	Fourth Figure
Barbara	Cesare	Datisi	Calemes
Celarent	Camestres	Feriso	Fresison
Darii	Festino	Disamis	Dimatis
Ferio	Baroco	Bocardo	Bamalip
		Darapti	Fesapo
		Felapton	

This table of syllogisms will now be tested by means of the predicate calculus to determine whether it really contains all admissible syllogisms, and whether all of the syllogisms it contains satisfy the requirement that the conclusion follows logically from the premises. For this purpose we will first of all represent the four forms A, I, E, O of a judgment AB in our symbolism. Letting X and Y stand for the predicates "is A" and "is B," the symbolic representations are:

$$| \overline{X} \vee Y | ; \quad | \overline{X \vee \overline{Y}} | ; \quad | \overline{X} \vee \overline{Y} | ; \quad | \overline{X \vee Y} |.$$

---

[1] It must be observed that fixing the order of S and P in the conclusion does not involve any loss of generality, since in fact a figure of inference with PS as the conclusion always results from one of the four figures mentioned by mere change of notation and interchange of the premises.

From this notation we obtain immediately the classical rules of *Opposition* and *Conversion* for the forms of judgment under consideration. For, of the four judgments, the last is expressed as the contradictory of the first and the second as the contradictory of the third. In addition, the two middle formulas are symmetric in X and Y, so that the judgment "Some A is B" proves to have the same meaning as "Some B is A," and likewise the judgment "No A is B" the same meaning as "No B is A." On the other hand, no such conversion is possible with the forms A and O.

This method of representing the four forms of judgment we now apply to the syllogisms by introducing the symbols X, Y, and Z for the predicates "is S," "is M," and "is P." Each figure then consists of three formulas. The first premise will be represented by one of the four forms:

$$| \overline{Y} \vee Z | ; \quad | \overline{Y} \vee \overline{Z} | ; \quad | \overline{Z} \vee Y | ; \quad | \overline{Z} \vee \overline{Y} |$$

or by its logical contradictory. Correspondingly, in the second premise we shall have one of the forms:

$$| \overline{Y} \vee X | ; \quad | \overline{Y} \vee \overline{X} | ; \quad | \overline{X} \vee Y | ; \quad | \overline{X} \vee \overline{Y} |$$

or its contradictory. As the conclusion, there will be, either negated or un-negated, one of the two forms:

$$| \overline{X} \vee \overline{Z} | ; \quad | \overline{X} \vee Z | .$$

(Note that X, Y, and Z can occur un-negated only as the second term of a combination.)

In addition to these formal conditions we have the additional requirement that the third formula be a consequence of the first two, in the sense that upon the substitution of particular predicates for X, Y, and Z the first two formulas cannot hold without the third formula holding also.

We now have to investigate how this requirement limits the totality of admissible combinations of formulas.

We remark that, in a formula, two terms connected by v may be interchanged without altering the truth value of the formula. Further, the order of the premises is not essential, and because of the generality with which the conclusion should hold, it makes no difference whether a predicate is rendered by U or by $\overline{U}$. On the basis of these facts, every pair of premises may be reduced to one of the following six normal forms:

I. $\quad |\,\overline{U} \vee \overline{V}\,|$ III. $\quad |\,\overline{\overline{U} \vee \overline{V}}\,|$ V. $\quad |\,\overline{\overline{U} \vee \overline{V}}\,|$

$\quad\quad |\,\overline{V} \vee \overline{W}\,|$ $\quad\quad |\,\overline{V} \vee \overline{W}\,|$ $\quad\quad |\,V \vee \overline{W}\,|$

II. $\quad |\,\overline{U} \vee \overline{V}\,|$ IV. $\quad |\,\overline{\overline{U} \vee \overline{V}}\,|$ VI. $\quad |\,\overline{\overline{U} \vee \overline{V}}\,|$

$\quad\quad |\,V \vee \overline{W}\,|$ $\quad\quad |\,V \vee \overline{W}\,|$ $\quad\quad |\,V \vee \overline{W}\,|$

The conclusion takes one of the forms (negated or unnegated)

$$|\,\overline{U} \vee \overline{W}\,| ;\quad |\,\overline{U} \vee W\,| ;\quad |\,U \vee \overline{W}\,| ;\quad |\,U \vee W\,|.$$

From this new notation we may return to the earlier one by first substituting either Y or $\overline{Y}$ for V, equating U, W or else W, U to one of the pairs $X, \overline{Z};\ \ \overline{X}, Z;\ \ X, Z;\ \ \overline{X}, \overline{Z}$, and then considering all possible transpositions of the disjuncts which (with a suitable order of the premises) lead to the formally admissible triads of formulas.

If now we test the six pairs of premises I.-VI. to see what conclusion may be drawn from each of them, we shall discover first of all that no conclusion of the required kind follows from I., IV., and V.

In fact, I. is satisfied by any arbitrary U and W, if the predicate V holds for no object. IV. is satisfied if V holds for all objects, provided only that U holds for at least one object. V. is satisfied for arbitrary U and W which hold for at least one object in case V holds for all objects.

The premises in VI. likewise fail to yield any of the conclusions considered. For in order that these premises be satisfied for properly chosen V, it is sufficient that U and W hold for one object each. However, these conditions are compatible with the falsehood of each of the conclusions in question.

Thus only cases II. and III. need be considered for our inferences. Using the abbreviation $\rightarrow$ and the first of the formulas on page 49, the two premises of II., $|\,\overline{U} \vee \overline{V}\,|$ and $|\,V \vee \overline{W}\,|$, immediately yield the relation $|\,\overline{U} \vee \overline{W}\,|$. Furthermore, $|\,\overline{U} \vee \overline{W}\,|$ is the strongest conclusion which may be drawn from the two premises, since if this relation is valid, the two premises are satisfied when we put V equal to W.

In III., the first premise $|\overline{\overline{U} \vee \overline{V}}|$ means that there are objects (*i.e.* at least one object) for which U and V both hold. The second premise, $|\overline{V} \vee \overline{W}|$, means that any object which has the property V also has the property $\overline{W}$. From this it follows that there are objects for which U and $\overline{W}$ both hold, *i.e.*, that $|\overline{\overline{U} \vee W}|$ is a true formula.

Conversely, if the formula $|\overline{UW}|$ is true, then the premises of III. are satisfied by putting $\overline{V}$ equal to W.

Hence, it follows that the syllogisms we are considering may be reduced to two principal forms, namely:

$$
\text{(A)} \quad \frac{\begin{array}{c} |\overline{U} \vee \overline{V}| \\ |V \vee \overline{W}| \end{array}}{|\overline{U} \vee \overline{W}|}
\qquad\qquad
\text{(B)} \quad \frac{\begin{array}{c} |\overline{\overline{U} \vee \overline{V}}| \\ |\overline{V} \vee \overline{W}| \end{array}}{|\overline{U} \vee W|}
$$

From these two principal forms we wish finally to pass, by means of the various admissible transformations, back to the earlier representations, which enable us to distinguish the several sorts of Aristotelian syllogisms. In doing so, we must bear in mind the formal restrictions on the syllogisms, to the effect that the un-negated predicates X, Y, and Z may enter into a product (disjunction) only as a second factor and that Y never occurs in a conclusion. Furthermore, we must note that the interchange of U and W in the principal form (A) does not furnish a new type of syllogism.

Accordingly, we obtain all the syllogisms arising from the principal form (A), by the following substitutions:

$$
\begin{array}{lll}
U = X, & V = Y, & W = Z; \\
U = X, & V = \overline{Y}, & W = Z; \\
U = X, & V = \overline{Y}, & W = \overline{Z}.
\end{array}
$$

Of these (with suitable ordering of the premises and of the factors), the first yields the syllogisms *Camestres* and *Calemes*, the second, *Celarent* and *Cesare*, the third, *Barbara*.

From the principal form (B) we obtain the various types of syllogisms by the substitutions:

$$U = X, \quad V = Y, \quad W = Z; \quad U = X, \quad V = Y, \quad W = \bar{Z};$$
$$U = X, \quad V = \bar{Y}, \quad W = Z; \quad U = Z, \quad V = Y, \quad W = \bar{X};$$
$$U = \bar{Z}, \quad V = Y, \quad W = \bar{X}.$$

The first substitution yields the syllogisms *Ferio*, *Festino*, *Feriso*, *Fresison*; the second, *Darii* and *Datisi*; the third, *Baroco*; the fourth, *Disamis* and *Dimatis*; the fifth, *Bocardo*.

The above discussion shows that there are fifteen syllogisms of the sort desired. All of these are Aristotelian syllogisms; hence, the classical list of syllogisms exhausts all possible cases. However, our method has not yielded all of the Aristotelian syllogisms. Rather, the four syllogisms, *Darapti*, *Bamalip*, *Felapton*, and *Fesapo*, are missing from the list just obtained. This discrepancy is due to the fact that the meaning of the universal affirmative statement ("All *A* is *B*"), traditional since Aristotle, is not fully consistent with our interpretation of the formula $| \bar{X} \vee Y |$. According to Aristotle the sentence "All *A* is *B*" is valid only when there are objects which are *A*. Our deviation from Aristotle in this respect is justified by the mathematical applications of logic, in which the Aristotelian interpretation would not be useful.

With this, we conclude our discussion of the predicate and class calculus. A number of interesting problems, it is true, might be proposed; *e.g.*, which formulas of the combined calculus constitute logically true sentences. However, we shall forego a closer examination of these problems, since they will be formulated and treated in a more general context in the next chapter. For example, the question of logically true formulas in the combined calculus will be completely answered in § 12 of the next chapter. We shall also forego an axiomatic treatment of the monadic predicate calculus.[1] The class calculus or monadic predicate cal-

---

[1] A complete axiom system for the combined calculus and at the same time an interesting extension of the class calculus has been given by M. Wajsberg in *Ein erweiterter Klassenkalkül*, Mh. Math. Physik Vol. 40 (1932) [See also the correction thereto in Mh. Math. Physik Vol. 42 (1935) p. 242]. The question likewise treated in that paper concerning the logically true sentences of the combined calculus had already been solved in another way in the papers (mentioned in § 12 of the next chapter) by Löwenheim, Skolem, and Behmann. Cf. especially that of Behmann in Math. Ann. Vol. 86 (1922).

culus is made superfluous in any case by the introduction, below, of the predicate calculus in the extended sense, for which it constitutes only a preparation, so that later we shall have no need to return to the matters treated in this chapter. It is quite otherwise with the sentential calculus, which remains the indispensable basis for all further investigation.

CHAPTER III

THE RESTRICTED PREDICATE CALCULUS

§ 1. The Inadequacy of the Foregoing Calculus

The combined calculus made possible a more systematic treatment of logical questions than the traditional intuitive logic. On the other hand, however, it may be said that the two are essentially the same as regards the possibility of drawing logical conclusions. The more complicated inferences which are possible in the combined calculus are also obtainable by a repeated application of the Aristotelian syllogisms.

In the opinion of earlier logicians, which Kant also shared, the Aristotelian theory of inference exhausted all of logic. Kant said:[1]

"It is remarkable that up to the present day [since Aristotle] it [logic] has not been able to make a single step forward, and thus, to all appearances, may be considered as completed and finished."

In reality the Aristotelian formalism turns out to be inadequate even in quite simple logical situations. It is basically insufficient for dealing with the logical foundations of mathematics. It fails, specifically, whenever a *relation among several objects* is to be represented symbolically.

This may be clarified by a simple example. Consider the statement: "If B lies between A and C, then B also lies between C and A." In the ordinary sentential calculus, it is true, this may be written in the form $X \to Y$; and the statement retains the same form in the monadic predicate calculus. In the latter it may in fact be formulated thus: "If an ordered triple of points

---

[1] In the preface to the second edition of the *Critique of Pure Reason*.

has the property that the second point lies between the first and third, then it also has the property that the second point lies between the third and first." This formulation, however, fails to express the logical essence of the statement, namely, the symmetry with respect to A and C of the relation "between." Therefore, it cannot be employed to derive the mathematical consequences of the statement under consideration. In this respect nothing is changed by using the formulation of the combined calculus.

In order to render this matter more explicit, another example, which incidentally does not belong to mathematics, may be given. "If there is a son, then there is a father," is certainly a logically self-evident assertion, and we may demand of any satisfactory logical calculus that it make obvious this self-evidence, in the sense that the asserted connection will be seen, by means of the symbolic representation, to be a consequence of simple logical principles. With our foregoing calculus, however, there can be no question of this. Of course, by the application of the combined calculus, we can render the asserted statement symbolically by the formula $| \overline{\overline{X}} | \rightarrow | \overline{Y} |$, in which X and Y stand respectively for the predicates "is a son," "is a father." But this formula certainly cannot help us to recognize the truth of the assertion, since it may yield false sentences when other substitutions are made for X and Y. The formula does not express that on which the logical connection between antecedent and consequent is based, namely, that the predicates "to be a son" and "to be a father" designate a relation of one object to another. A similar state of affairs is encountered with nearly all complicated statements.

§ 2. Methodological Basis of the Predicate Calculus

Since the foregoing calculus has turned out to be inadequate, we are forced to seek a new kind of logical symbolism. For this purpose we return to that point in our discussion at which we first went beyond the sentential calculus. The decisive step there was the division of sentences into subject and predicate. We have not, however, made full use of this division, since in our symbolic rendering of sentences we symbolized explicitly only the predicates but not the subjects. The reason for this limitation on the symbolism lay in the fact that as regards formalism we sought to follow the sentential calculus. If we abandon this point of view of analogy with the sentential calculus, then the following method seems a natural one: to separate in the rendering of a sentence the *objects* (*individuals*) from the *properties* (*predicates*) attributed to them and to symbolize both explicitly.

This is done by employing *functional symbols with argument places* (*n*-adic functional symbols where n is the number of argument places) for the symbolic rendering of predicates, in which symbols representing objects are to be substituted in the argument places. For example, the functional symbol $P(\ )$ may stand for the predicate "is a prime number." Then $P(5)$ stands for the sentence "5 is a prime number." If $M(\ )$ stands for the predicate "to be a man," then M(Socrates) means "Socrates is a man." Furthermore, if the relation of the smaller to the greater is expressed by the two-place functional symbol $<(\ ,\ )$, then $<(2, 3)$ is the symbolic rendering of the sentence "2 is less than 3." Likewise, the sentence "*B* lies between *A* and *C*" may be rendered by $Z(A, B, C)$.

All mathematical formulas represent such relations among two or more quantities. For example, to the formula $x + y = z$ there corresponds a triadic predicate $S(x, y, z)$. The truth of $S(x, y, z)$ means that x, y, and z are connected by the relation $x + y = z$.[1]

The connectives of the sentential calculus may be applied to sentences rendered in the new manner. For example, the contradictory of the sentence $P(5)$ is expressed by $\overline{P(5)}$. The formula

$$[<(2, 3)\ \&<(3, 7)] \rightarrow <(2, 7)$$

stands for the sentence "If 2 is less than 3 and 3 is less than 7, then 2 is less than 7."

A symbolic expression for the *universality of sentences* is still lacking. In order to obtain one we shall, following mathe-

---

[1] Hitherto it has been customary in logic to call only functions with one argument place predicates, while functions with more than one place were called relations. Here we use the word "predicate" in a quite general sense.

matics as a model, introduce—in addition to the symbols for definite objects (proper names)—*variables x, y, z, . . .* with which the
argument places of the functional symbols may likewise be filled.
A *definite* name substituted into an argument place designates a
value of the variable in question.

In general the values of a variable are limited to definite
kinds of objects, which are determined by the meaning of the
functional symbol. For example, the fundamental relation of
elementary plane geometry, "The point x lies on the line y," is
expressed by a functional symbol with two arguments, $L(x,y)$.
The values for x can only be points; those for y can only be
straight lines.

If definite value-expressions (*i.e.* proper names of individuals)
are substituted into the argument places of logical functions, then
definite sentences result, which may be either true or false. If, on
the other hand, the places of the functional symbols are filled by
variables, no definite judgment is represented thereby; we have,
rather, only a symbolic expression which depends upon the variables involved. We may proceed in the logical calculus just as we
do in algebra, where we write formulas with letters which mean
that for any arbitrary numerals that we substitute for the variables the resulting numerical equation is true. A formula such as

$$[< (x, y) \,\&< (y, z)] \to < (x, z)$$

then means that for any arbitrary triple of numbers x, y and z for
which the relations $< (x,y)$ and $< (y,z)$ hold, $< (x,z)$ is also true.

With this, we have already obtained a representation of universal judgments. However, in order to be able to use universal
sentences in combination with negation and the logical connectives &, v, and →, we need a *special "universal quantifier."* Other-
wise we could not tell whether $\overline{P(x)}$ means "for all x, $\overline{P(x)}$ is the
case," or, "It is not true that the sentence $P(x)$ holds for all x."
This representation of universal judments is secured by putting
the variable belonging to the logical function involved, in parentheses before the functional symbol.

$(x)A(x)$ thus means: For all x, $A(x)$ is true. The two judgments which gave rise to confusion just now are, then, differen-

tiated by $(x)\overline{P(x)}$ and $\overline{(x)P(x)}$. For reasons of symmetry we shall introduce at the same time a special *"existential quantifier"* for representing *particular* judgments. $(Ex)A(x)$ represents the judgment "There exists an x for which $A(x)$ is true."

The variable which belongs to a universal or an existential quantifier we shall call a *"bound variable."* It plays a role analogous to that of the variable of integration in mathematics; thus, for example, it makes no difference what letter is used for it. In contradistinction to the term "bound variables" we may call the others *"free variables."*

As to notation it should be observed that a formula which is preceded by a universal or an existential quantifier is to be placed in parentheses in case it contains one of the connectives &, v, and → and is not already held together by a negation bar. Furthermore, for brevity we establish the following conventions:

For $\overline{A(x)}$ we write $\overline{A}(x)$,
For $\overline{(x)A(x)}$ we write $\overline{(x)}A(x)$,
For $\overline{(Ex)A(x)}$ we write $\overline{(Ex)}A(x)$.

From the meaning of the universal and existential quantifiers, the following equivalences are obtained:

$$(Ex)A(x) \quad \text{eq.} \quad \overline{(x)}\overline{A}(x),$$
$$(Ex)\overline{A}(x) \quad \text{eq.} \quad \overline{(x)}A(x),$$
$$\overline{(Ex)}A(x) \quad \text{eq.} \quad (x)\overline{A}(x),$$
$$\overline{(Ex)}\overline{A}(x) \quad \text{eq.} \quad (x)A(x).$$

On the basis of these relations, the existential quantifier may be expressed in terms of the universal quantifier and vice versa. Thus the symbolism of the predicate calculus requires only three connectives. All we really need is the negation sign, one of the three signs &, v, and →, and finally one of the two signs (x) and (Ex).

Hitherto we have only considered cases in which universal and existential quantifiers appear singly. However, if we consider cases in which universal and existential quantifiers occur in combination, we are led to essentially new logical structures.

Such combinations are possible even in the case of one-place (monadic) predicates; they assume a special prominence in the case of many-place predicates. For a dyadic predicate $A(x, y)$, for example, the following are the simplest forms of combinations:

$$(x)(y)A(x, y)$$

"for all x and for all y the relation $A(x, y)$ holds";

$$(Ex)(Ey)A(x, y)$$

"there is an x and there is a y for which $A(x, y)$ holds";

$$(x)(Ey)A(x, y)$$

"for every x there is a y such that $A(x, y)$ holds";

$$(Ex)(y)A(x, y)$$

"there is an x which stands to every y in the relation $A(x, y)$."

In order to clarify further the meaning of such combinations, one might insert a pair of brackets in each case so that, for example, we could write:

$$(x)[(y)A(x, y)],$$
$$(x)[(Ey)A(x, y)].$$

But since there is no basis for misunderstanding, it is customary to omit the brackets. If combinations of three or more quantifiers are admitted, then there is a correspondingly greater multiplicity of combinations.

From the meaning of the universal quantifier it follows that in an expression $(x)(y)A(x, y)$ *the two universal quantifiers may be interchanged without altering the sense of the sentence.* This also holds for the two existential quantifiers in an expression such as

$$(Ex)(Ey)A(x, y).$$

In $(x)(Ey)A(x, y)$, however, the order of the symbols (x) and (Ey) is essential.

For example, the expression

$$(x)(Ey) < (x, y),$$

where x and y are variables referring to the domain of real numbers, constitutes a *true* sentence, namely, "For every number x

there is a number y such that x is less than y," *i.e.* "Given any number there is a greater one."

However if the order of the symbols (x) and (Ey) is changed in this case, we obtain $(Ey)(x) < (x, y)$, which expresses a *false* sentence, namely, "There is a number y which is greater than every number x." By transposing (x) and (Ey), therefore, we get a quite different sentence.

The logical situation here is this, that on the basis of the theorem (to be proved later)

$$(Ey)(x)A(x, y) \rightarrow (x)(Ey)A(x, y),$$

$(x)(Ey)A(x, y)$ may be derived from a true sentence of the form $(Ey)(x)A(x, y)$, but not conversely.

§ 3. Preliminary Orientation on the Use of the Predicate Calculus

Before giving a systematic treatment of the rules which are necessary for manipulation in the predicate calculus, the consideration of a few examples will serve to make us more familiar with the symbolism.

We shall show, to begin with, how *the axioms which express the basic properties of the sequence of natural numbers* may be rendered symbolically in the predicate calculus. These axioms are:

1. *For each number there is one and only one successor.*

2. *There is no number of which 1 is the immediate successor.*

3. *For each number other than 1 there is one and only one immediate predecessor.*

In these statements there occur predicate constants designating the relations, for numbers, of being the immediate successor of and of being distinct from. The relation of distinctness is involved not only in the meaning of the phrase "other than 1" but also implicitly in that of the expression "only one number," for, to say there is "only one" number with a certain property means that there are not two distinct such numbers. Being distinct is the opposite of being arithmetically equal.

We therefore introduce the predicates:

$$=(x, y) \quad (\text{"}x \text{ equals } y\text{"}),$$
$$I(x, y) \quad (\text{"}y \text{ is the immediate successor of } x\text{"}).$$

With this notation the above axioms may be written as follows:

1. $(x)(Ey)\{I(x, y) \mathbin{\&} (z)(I(x, z) \to =(y, z))\},$

that is, "For every x there is a y which is the immediate successor of x and which equals any z which is the immediate successor of x."

2. $\overline{(Ex)}I(x, 1),$

that is, "There is no x of which 1 is the immediate successor."

3. $(x)\{\overline{=(x, 1)} \to (Ey)[I(y, x) \mathbin{\&} (z)(I(z, x) \to =(y, z))]\},$

that is, "For every x distinct from 1, there is a y of which x is the immediate successor and which equals any z of which x is the immediate successor."

We shall next orient ourselves with regard to the *methods of proof* in the predicate calculus, by a few simple examples. We begin with the sentence whose unprovability in the calculus of the second chapter was one of the facts which established the inadequacy of that calculus. The sentence read, "If there is a son, then there is a father." The symbolic rendering of this assertion in the predicate calculus is:

$$(Ex)S(x) \to (Ex)F(x).$$

$S(x)$ stands for "x is a son," and $F(x)$, for "x is a father." A proof of this statement is possible only if we analyze conceptually the meanings of the two predicates which occur. In the concept "son" is contained the property "male," on the one hand, and, on the other, the relation of child to parents; in the concept "father," the relation to wife and child.

Accordingly, if we introduce for "x is male" the symbol $M(x)$ and render the predicate "x and y are the parents of z" (or more exactly, "x and y as husband and wife have z as their child") by the symbol $C(x, y, z)$, then we define $S(x)$ *by*

$$M(x) \mathbin{\&} (Eu)(Ev)C(u, v, x).$$

("x is a son" means, "x is male, and there is a u and there is a v such that u as husband and v as wife are the parents of x.")

Likewise $F(x)$ is defined by

$$(Ey)(Ez)C(x, y, z).$$

("x is a father" means, "There is a y and there is a z such that x and y as husband and wife are the parents of z.")

If we introduce the expressions obtained for $S(x)$ and $F(x)$, the above assertion assumes the form:

$$(Ex)[M(x) \ \& \ (Eu)(Ev)C(u,v,x)] \to (Ex)(Ey)(Ez)C(x,y,z).$$

This formula sets forth an implication between two sentences; for its proof, we have to obtain the second from the first by a series of implications each of which is based on the rules of the calculus. To this end we use the principle which we know from the sentential calculus, and which of course is also valid in the predicate calculus, namely, that from two implications $\mathfrak{A} \to \mathfrak{B}$ and $\mathfrak{B} \to \mathfrak{C}$, we may always infer $\mathfrak{A} \to \mathfrak{C}$.

Now, to begin with, we have in the predicate calculus the formula

$$(Ex)\big(G(x) \ \& \ H(x)\big) \to (Ex)H(x),$$

valid for arbitrary G and H and corresponding to the sentential formula $X \ \& \ Y \to Y$.

If we put $N(x)$ as an abbreviation for the expression $(Eu)(Ev)C(u, v, x)$, which is a predicate of x, we obtain

$$S(x) \quad \text{eq.} \quad M(x) \ \& \ N(x).$$

The above implication then gives

$$(Ex)S(x) \to (Ex)N(x),$$

or, by substituting the expression for $N(x)$,

$$(Ex)S(x) \to (Ex)(Eu)(Ev)C(u, v, x).$$

Now there is a general theorem of the predicate calculus to the effect that in an uninterrupted sequence of existential quantifiers the order of the quantifiers is immaterial. We have already noted this theorem in the case of two existential quantifiers. The general theorem is obtained therefrom by repeated application. If we make such a rearrangement, we obtain, in place of the last formula,

$$(Ex)S(x) \to (Eu)(Ev)(Ex)C(u, v, x).$$

This, however, is our original assertion, apart from the fact that the variables after the $\rightarrow$ are written differently.

A further example is furnished by the assertion

"Where there is an effect, there is a cause."

This assertion may first be written in the form:

$$(Ex)\,R\,(x) \rightarrow (Ex)\,C\,(x).$$

$R(x)$ means, "x is an effect," and $C(x)$, "x is a cause." We now again analyse the predicates C and R by the introduction of the dyadic predicate "x produces y" for which we choose the symbol $P(x, y)$. If we do this, we get for $C(x)$ and $R(x)$ the defining expressions:

$$C(x) \quad \text{eq.} \quad (Ey)\,P(x, y)$$

and

$$R(x) \quad \text{eq.} \quad (Ey)\,P(y, x).$$

By the substitution of these expressions, we bring the assertion into the following form:

$$(Ex)\,(Ey)\,P(y, x) \rightarrow (Ex)\,(Ey)\,P(x, y)$$

or, rewriting the variables on the left-hand side,

$$(Ey)\,(Ex)\,P(x, y) \rightarrow (Ex)\,(Ey)\,P(x, y).$$

This formula is an immediate consequence of the theorem about rearrangement of existential quantifiers.

The distinction between $(Ex)\,(y)\,A\,(x, y)$ and $(y)\,(Ex)\,A\,(x, y)$, mentioned earlier, may also be illustrated by the example of *uniform and ordinary convergence*. We consider a definite sequence of single-valued functions $f_1(x)$, $f_2(x)$, ... whose values are real numbers and which (as we shall assume for simplicity) are defined for all real values of x. The assertion that this sequence of functions converges to 0 for every value of x may be formulated in our symbolism thus:

$$(x)\,(z)\,\{< (0, z) \rightarrow (Ey)\,(n)\,[< (y, n) \rightarrow <\,(\,|\,f_n(x)\,|\,,\,z)\,]\}$$

("For an arbitrary x, there is, for every z greater than 0, a y such that for all n greater than y, the inequality $|\,f_n(x)\,| < z$ is satisfied"). Here the variables y and n are integers, while x and z are real numbers.

For the assertion that the sequence of functions converges *uniformly* to 0 for all values of x, the symbolic expression is:

$$(z)\{<(0, z) \to (Ey)(x)(n)[<(y, n) \to <(|f_n(x)|, z)]\}$$

("For every z greater than 0, there is a y such that for all x and for all n greater than y, the inequality $|f_n(x)| < z$ is satisfied").

The distinction between the two assertions finds its expression in the different positions of the universal quantifier (x).

§ 4. Precise Notation for the Predicate Calculus

By way of preparation for a systematic treatment of the predicate calculus, we first give an exact survey of the notations employed.

Among the symbols which occur in the predicate calculus there are first of all *variables* of different kinds. The variables are always capital or small italic letters. We distinguish among:

1. *Sentential variables*: $X, Y, Z, \ldots$
2. *Individual variables*: $x, y, z, \ldots$
3. *Predicate variables*: $F(\,.\,), G(\,.\,,.\,), H(\,.\,,.\,,.\,), \ldots$

Here, predicate variables with different numbers of argument places always count as distinct variables, even when the capital italic letters are the same.

We now wish to explain what is to be understood by a *formula* of the predicate calculus.

First of all, we say provisionally that we are to understand by a formula an expression constructed in a meaningful manner from the above variables by means of the sentential connectives &, v, ⎯, →, and ∼, and of the universal and existential quantifiers. However, the preservation of the axiomatic standpoint set forth in the following section, in which the proofs follow from purely formal rules without appeal to the meaning of the logical symbols, makes it necessary to characterize the expressions designated as formulas by a description of their formal structure only, and to avoid concepts such as "meaningful."

To begin with, we say this about the general appearance of the formulas, namely, that there may occur in them individual variables (*i.e.* small italic letters) and corresponding universal and existential quantifiers. Now if there occurs in a formula, simultaneously with an individual variable, say x, a corresponding universal or existential quantifier—in this case, therefore, (x) or (Ex)—then the variable in question within the formula is called *bound*, and otherwise, *free*.

By the term *formula* we now understand those, and only those, combinations of symbols of our calculus which may be shown to be such by a finite number of applications of the following rules:

1. A sentential variable is a formula;

2. Predicate variables whose argument places are filled by individual variables, are formulas;

3. If any combination $\mathfrak{A}$ of symbols is a formula, then $\overline{\mathfrak{A}}$ is also a formula;

4. If $\mathfrak{A}$ and $\mathfrak{B}$ are any formulas such that the same individual variable does not occur bound in one of them and free in the other, then

$$\mathfrak{A} \,\&\, \mathfrak{B}, \ \mathfrak{A} \,v\, \mathfrak{B}, \ \mathfrak{A} \to \mathfrak{B}, \text{ and } \mathfrak{A} \sim \mathfrak{B}$$

are also formulas;

5. If $\mathfrak{A}(x)$ is any formula in which the variable x occurs as a free variable, then $(x)\mathfrak{A}(x)$ and $(Ex)\mathfrak{A}(x)$ are also formulas. The corresponding statement holds for other free variables.

We explicitly call attention to the fact that according to this definition the same variable cannot occur in a single formula both free and bound.

In order to save parentheses, we agree on the following conventions: In the grouping of expressions, the connectives $\to$, v, $\&$, and $\sim$ shall have precedence over the universal and existential quantifiers. For example, $(x)F(x) \,\&\, A$ is a simpler way of writing $((x)F(x)) \,\&\, A$. We retain the earlier conventions that $\to$ and $\sim$ have precedence over $\&$; and $\&$, in turn, over v. Further, to each universal or existential quantifier occurring in a formula, there belongs a definite constituent part of the formula to which it relates. We shall call this part the *scope* of the symbol in question. Thus in the formula

$$(x)\left(F(x) \to (Ey)G(y)\right),$$

the scope of the symbol (x) extends to the end of the formula, while in

$$(x)F(x) \to (Ey)G(y),$$

it extends only up to the symbol $\to$. We can further reduce the number of parentheses by adopting the following rule: If we have several universal or existential quantifiers in succession not separated by parentheses, then it is always to be understood that their scopes extend to the same point. Thus, for example,

$$(x)(Ey)(z)\left(H(x, y, z) \,\&\, K(y, z)\right) \,\&\, L(u)$$

is a simpler way of writing

$$(x)\{(Ey)[(z)(H(x, y, z) \,\&\, K(y, z))]\} \,\&\, L(u).$$

To avoid misunderstanding, we shall explain once more the use of *capital German letters*, as we have already briefly done earlier (in Chap. I, § 5) for the sentential calculus. These letters are not symbols of our language of formulas, and in principle we could do without them altogether. They serve only to give a short expression for the content of statements about the calculus. In such statements, we let $\mathfrak{A}$, $\mathfrak{B}$, and $\mathfrak{C}$ designate any formulas whatever whose exact form is left unspecified. For example, $\mathfrak{A} \to \mathfrak{B}$ represents any implication, *e.g.* $(A \to B) \to (B \to C)$ or $(x)F(x) \to (x)G(x)$. We designate by $\mathfrak{A}(x)$ any formula which contains the free variable x; likewise, by $\mathfrak{A}(x, y)$, any formula in which the free variables x and y occur, and so forth.

§ 5. The Axioms of the Predicate Calculus

We will now proceed, just as we did for the sentential calculus, to set up for the predicate calculus a system of axioms from which the remaining true sentences of the predicate calculus may be obtained by means of certain rules.

The setting up of the axioms and of the rules of inference is of course done in conformity with the intuitive or objective interpretation of the formulas. However, the deduction of the "true" formulas from the axioms must be purely formal, in accordance with the axiomatic point of view, so that we are not at all con-cerned with the meaning of the sentences symbolized by the formulas, but solely with following the prescriptions contained in the rules. Only in the interpretation of the results obtained by the formal operations should we take into account the meaning of the symbols of our calculus.

This interpretation as to content is made as follows. We con-sider as given a domain of individuals, to which the individual variables and the universal and existential quantifiers refer. This domain is left unspecified; we assume only that it contains at least one individual. A formula of the predicate calculus is called logically true or, as we also say, *universally valid* only if, inde-pendently of the choice of the domain of individuals, the formula always becomes a true sentence for any substitution of definite sentences, of names of individuals belonging to the domain of individuals, and of predicates defined over the domain of indi-viduals, for the sentential variables, the free individual variables, and the predicate variables respectively. The universally valid formulas of the predicate calculus will also, for convenience, sometimes be called simply *valid*.

We now state the system of axioms for the predicate calculus. As primitive logical formulas, we first have the axioms of the sentential calculus, which for the sake of simplicity we shall give in the same form as before.

a) $X \vee X \to X$.

b) $X \to X \vee Y$.

c) $X \vee Y \to Y \vee X$.

d) $(X \to Y) \to (Z \vee X \to Z \vee Y)$.

($\mathfrak{A} \to \mathfrak{B}$ is again to be understood as an abbreviation for $\overline{\mathfrak{A}} \vee \mathfrak{B}$.)

In addition, we now have a group of two *axioms for "all" and "there exists"* (the universal and existential quantifiers).

e) $(x) F(x) \to F(y)$.

f) $F(y) \to (Ex) F(x)$.

The first of these axioms means, "If a predicate F holds for all x, then it also holds for any arbitrary y."

The second formula means, "If a predicate F holds for some particular y, then there is an x for which F holds."

We have the following rules for obtaining new formulas from the primitive logical formulas, as well as from formulas obtained therefrom.

a) Rules of Substitution

$a1$)   A sentential variable occurring in a formula may be replaced by any formula, if the replacement be simultaneously effected at all the occurrences of the sentential variable, provided that the result of the substitution is a formula in the sense of the definition of the previous section. In addition, the substitution is permitted only when the formula to be substituted contains no individual variable which appears as a bound variable in the original formula.

$a2$)   A free individual variable may be replaced by any other individual variable, provided that the replacement be simultaneously effected at all the occurrences of the free variable and that the substituted variable have no bound occurrence in the original formula.

$a3$)   Under certain circumstances, a predicate variable with n argument places may be replaced by a formula which contains at least n free individual variables. Let F be the n-adic predicate variable, and $\mathfrak{A}$ the formula in which F is to be replaced. From among the individual variables occurring in the formula which is to replace F, we select any n whatsoever ordered in any arbitrary way, say, $x_1, x_2, \ldots, x_n$. The formula which is to be substituted will accordingly be designated by $\mathfrak{B}(x_1, x_2, \ldots, x_n)$. The substitution is now permissible only if the remaining free individual variables which may still occur in $\mathfrak{B}(x_1, x_2, \ldots, x_n)$ do not occur in the formula $\mathfrak{A}$ as bound variables, and if, further, there is no occurrence of F in $\mathfrak{A}$ such that a variable occupying an argument place in F occurs as a bound variable in $\mathfrak{B}(x_1, x_2, \ldots, x_n)$,[1] provided always that the result of the substitution is a formula. The substitution is accomplished as follows: Considering any specific occurrence of the predicate variable F in $\mathfrak{A}$, we find the argument places of F occupied by certain individual variables, which we designate, for the moment, by $\mathfrak{a}_1, \mathfrak{a}_2, \ldots, \mathfrak{a}_n$. These need not all be different. We now replace $F(\mathfrak{a}_1, \mathfrak{a}_2, \ldots, \mathfrak{a}_n)$, at this occurrence of F, by $\mathfrak{B}(\mathfrak{a}_1, \mathfrak{a}_2, \ldots, \mathfrak{a}_n)$, *i.e.* by the formula obtained from $\mathfrak{B}(x_1, x_2, \ldots, x_n)$ when the variables $x_1, x_2, \ldots, x_n$ are replaced, wherever they occur, by $\mathfrak{a}_1, \mathfrak{a}_2, \ldots, \mathfrak{a}_n$ respectively. The corresponding substitution is to be made at every occurrence of F.

β) Rule of Implication

From two formulas of the form $\mathfrak{A}$ and $\mathfrak{A} \to \mathfrak{B}$, the new formula $\mathfrak{B}$ is obtained.

γ) Rules for the Universal and Existential Quantifiers

$\gamma 1$) From a formula $\mathfrak{A} \to \mathfrak{B}(x)$ in which the part after the $\to$ contains the free variable x while x does not occur in $\mathfrak{A}$, the formula $\mathfrak{A} \to (x)\mathfrak{B}(x)$ is obtained.

$\gamma 2$) Under the same hypotheses concerning $\mathfrak{A}$ and $\mathfrak{B}(x)$, a formula $\mathfrak{B}(x) \to \mathfrak{A}$ yields the new formula $(Ex)\mathfrak{B}(x) \to \mathfrak{A}$.[2]

δ) Rules for Rewriting Bound Variables

We may replace a bound individual variable occurring in a formula by any other bound variable. This replacement must be made simultaneously in the universal or existential quantifier involved and in all argument places in its scope. It is assumed for the admissibility of this replacement that the result is itself a formula. If the variable to be replaced occurs in more than one scope, then the replacement need be made in one scope only.

---

[1] Cf. A. Church, *Introduction to Mathematical Logic*, Part I, p. 63 (Princeton, 1944).—*Ed.*

[2] The axiom system for universal and existential quantifiers used here, which is expressed in formulas e) and f) as well as in Rules γ), is due to P. Bernays.

§ 6. The System of Universally Valid Formulas

We shall now see how, by means of the primitive logical formulas and rules of inference given, the entire system of *universally valid* formulas of the predicate calculus can be constructed.

We are already familiar with a sub-system of these formulas, namely that in which only sentential variables occur. We have already proved Theorems 1 through 20 and Rules I through VIII for this sub-system. This sub-system will be called the system of *universally valid formulas of the sentential calculus.*

First of all, we shall exhibit by means of various examples the method by which one must proceed in proving theorems. We shall next obtain, as we did in the sentential calculus, new rules of inference. In this we shall employ the theorems and rules, proved above, of the sentential calculus.

RULE γ'). *Let a formula* $\mathfrak{A}(x)$, *containing the free variable* x, *be a theorem; then* $(x)\mathfrak{A}(x)$ *is also a theorem.*

Proof: From $\mathfrak{A}(x)$ we obtain by application of Rules II and III

$$\overline{X \vee \overline{X}} \vee \mathfrak{A}(x),$$

$$\overline{X \vee \overline{X}} \vee (x)\mathfrak{A}(x) \qquad \text{[by Rule } \gamma)\,],$$

$$\overline{X} \vee \overline{X} \qquad \text{[Theorem 3]},$$

$$(x)\mathfrak{A}(x) \qquad \text{[Rule of Implication]}.$$

RULE δ'). *One may replace all the free and bound variables of a formula by other variables, taking care only that any variable is replaced at each occurrence by the same new variable and that different variables are replaced by different variables.*

The proof is obtained by repeated application of $\alpha 2)$ and $\delta)$. For example, the theorem $(y)F(y) \to F(x)$ is obtained from the primitive formula e) in the following way:

$$(x)F(x) \to F(y),$$

$$(x)F(x) \to F(z) \qquad \text{[Rule } \alpha 2)\,],$$

$$(y)F(y) \to F(z) \qquad \text{[Rule } \delta)\,],$$

$$(y)F(y) \to F(x) \qquad \text{[Rule } \alpha 2)\,].$$

It follows from Rule δ') that Rule γ) remains valid if in the formulation of the rule one consistently puts y, or any other variable, in place of x.

THEOREM 21. $(x)\left(F(x) \vee \overline{F}(x)\right)$.
Proof:

$$X \vee \overline{X} \qquad\qquad \text{[Theorem 3]},$$
$$F(x) \vee \overline{F}(x) \qquad\qquad \text{[by substitution]},$$
$$(x)\left(F(x) \vee \overline{F}(x)\right) \qquad\qquad \text{[by Rule } \gamma') \text{]}.$$

THEOREM 22. $(x)F(x) \to (Ex)F(x)$.
Proof:

$$(x)F(x) \to F(y) \qquad\qquad \text{[Axiom e)]},$$
$$F(y) \to (Ex)F(x) \qquad\qquad \text{[Axiom f)]},$$
$$(x)F(x) \to (Ex)F(x) \qquad\qquad \text{[Rule V]}.$$

THEOREM 23. $(x)\left(A \vee F(x)\right) \to A \vee (x)F(x)$.
Proof:

$$(y)\left(A \vee F(y)\right) \to A \vee F(x) \quad \text{[substitution in}$$
$$\text{Axiom e), and Rule } \delta') \text{]},$$
$$(y)\left(A \vee F(y)\right) \to \overline{\overline{A}} \vee F(x) \quad \text{[substitution of}$$
$$\overline{\overline{A}} \text{ for } A \text{]}.$$

Using the abbreviation $\to$ one may also write:

$$(y)\left(A \vee F(y)\right) \to \left(\overline{A} \to F(x)\right),$$
$$\left[(y)\left(A \vee F(y)\right) \& \overline{A}\right] \to F(x) \quad \text{[by Rule VII]},$$
$$\left[(y)\left(A \vee F(y)\right) \& \overline{A}\right] \to (x)F(x) \quad \text{[Rule } \gamma) \text{]}.$$

By means of Rule VII and Rule δ), this may be transformed back into

$$(x)\left(A \vee F(x)\right) \to A \vee (x)F(x).$$

THEOREM 24. $(x)\left(A \to F(x)\right) \to \left(A \to (x)F(x)\right)$.

Proof: This theorem is obtained from the preceding one by the substitution of $\overline{A}$ for A.

RULE IX. *If* $\mathfrak{A} \to (\mathfrak{B} \to \mathfrak{C}(x))$ *is a theorem, then the same is true of* $\mathfrak{A} \to (\mathfrak{B} \to (x)\mathfrak{C}(x))$. Here $\mathfrak{A}$ and $\mathfrak{B}$ must not contain the variable x.

This is an extension of Rule $\gamma 1$). Instead of two antecedents, we may also take any other finite number. The proof corresponds exactly to the case of two.

Proof:

$$\mathfrak{A} \to (\mathfrak{B} \to \mathfrak{C}(x)),$$
$$\mathfrak{A} \to (x)(\mathfrak{B} \to \mathfrak{C}(x)) \qquad [\text{Rule } \gamma)].$$

The desired formula results from this by application of Theorem 24 and Rule V.

THEOREM 25. $A \to (x)\big(A \vee F(x)\big)$.
Proof:

$$A \to A \vee B \qquad\qquad [\text{Axiom b})],$$
$$A \to A \vee F(x) \qquad\qquad [\text{by substitution}],$$
$$A \to (x)\big(A \vee F(x)\big) \qquad\qquad [\text{by Rule } \gamma)]$$

THEOREM 26. $(x)\big(A \vee F(x)\big) \sim A \vee (x)F(x)$.

Proof: Since Theorem 23 is proved, it is sufficient to prove its converse $A \vee (x)F(x) \to (x)\big(A \vee F(x)\big)$.

$$(y)F(y) \to F(x) \quad [\text{from e) by Rule } \delta')],$$
$$A \vee (y)F(y) \to A \vee F(x) \qquad [\text{by Rule IV}],$$
$$A \vee (x)F(x) \to (x)\big(A \vee F(x)\big) \qquad [\text{by Rules } \gamma)$$
$$\text{and } \delta)].$$

THEOREM 27. $(x)\big(A \to F(x)\big) \sim \big(A \to (x)F(x)\big)$.

Proof: This theorem is obtained from Theorem 26 in the same way as Theorem 24 is obtained from Theorem 23.

THEOREM 28. $(x)\big(A \,\&\, F(x)\big) \sim A \,\&\, (x)F(x)$.

Proof: We first prove:

I. $(x)(A \& F(x)) \to A \& (x)F(x)$.

   $(y)(A \& F(y)) \to A \& F(x)$,

   $\qquad A \& F(x) \to F(x) \qquad$ [Theorem 13],

   $\qquad (y)(A \& F(y)) \to F(x) \qquad$ [Rule V],

   $(x)(A \& F(x)) \to (x)F(x) \quad$ [Rules γ) and δ)],

   $\qquad A \& F(x) \to A$,

   $\qquad (x)(A \& F(x)) \to A \qquad$ [Rules V and δ)].

By using the theorem of the sentential calculus

$$(X \to Y) \to [(X \to Z) \to (X \to Y \& Z)],$$

and by a double application of the Rule of Implication we obtain formula I from the last formula and the second from last.

II. $A \& (x)F(x) \to (x)(A \& F(x))$.

   $(y)F(y) \to F(x)$;

from this one obtains by the sentential calculus

$$A \& (y)F(y) \to A \& F(x),$$

$$A \& (x)F(x) \to (x)(A \& F(x)) \qquad \text{[Rules } \gamma)$$
$$\text{and } \delta)].$$

From formulas I and II the theorem follows.

THEOREM 29. $(x)(y)F(x, y) \sim (y)(x)F(x, y)$.

Proof:

   $(z)(u)F(z, u) \to (u)F(x, u) \quad$ [substitution in
   $\qquad\qquad\qquad\qquad\qquad$ Axiom e) and Rule δ'],

   $\qquad (u)F(x, u) \to F(x, y) \qquad$ [substitution in
   $\qquad\qquad\qquad\qquad\qquad$ Axiom e) and Rule δ'],

   $(z)(u)F(z, u) \to F(x, y) \qquad$ [by Rule V]

   $(z)(u)F(z, u) \to (x)F(x, y) \qquad$ [Rule γ)],

   $(x)(y)F(x, y) \to (y)(x)F(x, y) \qquad$ [Rules γ)
   $\qquad\qquad\qquad\qquad\qquad\qquad\qquad$ and δ)].

Likewise we obtain $(y)(x)F(x, y) \to (x)(y)F(x, y)$ and thus also Theorem 29.

THEOREM 30. $(x)(F(x) \& G(x)) \sim (x)F(x) \& (x)G(x)$.

Proof: We first show

a) $(x)(F(x) \& G(x)) \to (x)F(x) \& (x)G(x)$.

$(y)(F(y) \& G(y)) \to F(x) \& G(x)$,

$F(x) \& G(x) \to F(x)$,

$F(x) \& G(x) \to G(x)$,

$(y)(F(y) \& G(y)) \to F(x)$ [by Rule V],

$(y)(F(y) \& G(y)) \to G(x)$ [by Rule V],

By Rules γ) and δ), both formulas may be changed to:

$(x)(F(x) \& G(x)) \to (x)F(x)$.

$(x)(F(x) \& G(x)) \to (x)G(x)$.

From both together one obtains

$(x)(F(x) \& G(x)) \to (x)F(x) \& (x)G(x)$.

b) Proof of

$(x)F(x) \& (x)G(x) \to (x)(F(x) \& G(x))$.

$(y)F(y) \to F(x)$,

$(y)G(y) \to G(x)$,

$(y)F(y) \& (y)G(y) \to F(x) \& G(x)$,

$(x)F(x) \& (x)G(x) \to (x)(F(x) \& G(x))$ [Rules γ) and δ)].

From a) and b) we obtain the theorem.

THEOREM 31.

$(x)(F(x) \to G(x)) \to ((x)F(x) \to (x)G(x))$.

Proof:

$(y)(F(y) \to G(y)) \to (F(x) \to G(x))$,

$F(x) \to ((y)(F(y) \to G(y)) \to G(x))$ [by Rule VII],

$(y)F(y) \to F(x)$,

$(y)F(y) \to ((y)(F(y) \to G(y)) \to G(x))$ [Rule V],

$$(y) F(y) \ \& \ (y) \left(F(y) \rightarrow G(y) \right) \rightarrow G(x) \quad \text{[Rule VII]},$$

$$(x) F(x) \ \& \ (x) \left(F(x) \rightarrow G(x) \right) \rightarrow (x) G(x) \quad \text{[Rules } \gamma)$$
$$\text{and } \delta)\,],$$

$$(x) \left(F(x) \rightarrow G(x) \right) \rightarrow \left((x) F(x) \rightarrow (x) G(x) \right) \quad \text{[Rule}$$
$$\text{VII].}$$

THEOREM 32.

$$(x) \left(F(x) \sim G(x) \right) \rightarrow \left((x) F(x) \sim (x) G(x) \right).$$

Proof:

$$(x) \left(F(x) \sim G(x) \right)$$

is an abbreviation for

$$(x) \left[\left(F(x) \rightarrow G(x) \right) \ \& \ \left(G(x) \rightarrow F(x) \right) \right].$$

By substitution in Theorem 30 we obtain:

$$(x) \left[\left(F(x) \rightarrow G(x) \right) \ \& \ \left(G(x) \rightarrow F(x) \right) \right] \sim$$
$$(x) \left(F(x) \rightarrow G(x) \right) \ \& \ (x) \left(G(x) \rightarrow F(x) \right).$$

By Theorem 31:

$$(x) \left(F(x) \rightarrow G(x) \right) \rightarrow \left((x) F(x) \rightarrow (x) G(x) \right),$$
$$(x) \left(G(x) \rightarrow F(x) \right) \rightarrow \left((x) G(x) \rightarrow (x) F(x) \right).$$

Thus we have three formulas of the form:

$$\mathfrak{A} \sim \mathfrak{B} \ \& \ \mathfrak{C},$$
$$\mathfrak{B} \rightarrow (\mathfrak{D} \rightarrow \mathfrak{E}),$$
$$\mathfrak{C} \rightarrow (\mathfrak{E} \rightarrow \mathfrak{D}).$$

From these we may obtain $\mathfrak{A} \rightarrow (\mathfrak{D} \sim \mathfrak{E})$. That, however, constitutes our theorem, if we replace $\mathfrak{A}$, $\mathfrak{D}$, and $\mathfrak{E}$ by the formulas which they represent.

THEOREM 33.

a) $(Ex) F(x) \sim \overline{(x)} \, \overline{F}(x).$

b) $(Ex) \overline{F}(x) \sim \overline{(x)} F(x).$

c) $\overline{(Ex)} \, \overline{F}(x) \sim (x) F(x).$

d) $\overline{(Ex)} F(x) \sim (x) \overline{F}(x).$

Proof of 33a) :

$$(y)\overline{F}(y) \to \overline{F}(x),$$

$$\overline{\overline{F}}(x) \to \overline{(y)}\,\overline{F}(y) \qquad \text{[by Theorem 6],}$$

$$F(x) \to \overline{(y)}\,\overline{F}(y) \qquad \text{[substitution of}$$

$$F(x) \text{ for } \overline{\overline{F}}(x)\,],$$

$$(Ex)F(x) \to \overline{(x)}\,\overline{F}(x) \qquad \text{[by Rules } \gamma)$$

$$\text{and } \delta)\,].$$

This is the first half of Theorem 33a).

$$F(x) \to (Ey)F(y) \qquad \text{[from Axiom f)],}$$

$$\overline{(Ey)}F(y) \to \overline{F}(x) \qquad \text{[by Theorem 6],}$$

$$\overline{(Ex)}F(x) \to (x)\overline{F}(x) \qquad \text{[Rules } \gamma) \text{ and } \delta)\,],$$

$$\overline{(x)}\,\overline{F}(x) \to \overline{\overline{(Ex)}}F(x) \qquad \text{[by Theorem 6],}$$

$$\overline{(x)}\,\overline{F}(x) \to (Ex)F(x) \qquad \text{[substitution of}$$

$$(Ex)F(x) \text{ for } \overline{\overline{(Ex)}}F(x)\,],$$

This is the other half of Theorem 33a)

Proof of 33b) :

$$A \sim \overline{\overline{A}},$$

$$F(x) \sim \overline{\overline{F}}(x) \qquad \text{[by substitution],}$$

$$(x)\,(F(x) \sim \overline{\overline{F}}(x)) \qquad \text{[Rule } \gamma')\,].$$

Using Theorem 32, we obtain from this:

$$(x)F(x) \sim (x)\overline{\overline{F}}(x),$$

$$\overline{(x)}F(x) \sim \overline{(x)}\,\overline{\overline{F}}(x)$$

[making use of $(X \sim Y) \to (\overline{X} \sim \overline{Y})$, cf. formula (26) page 9].

By substitution in 33a) we obtain:

$$(Ex)\overline{F}(x) \sim \overline{(x)}\,\overline{\overline{F}}(x),$$

thus

$$\overline{(x)}F(x) \sim (Ex)\overline{F}(x).$$

This is Theorem 33b).

From Theorems 33a) and 33b) we also obtain Theorems 33d) and 33c), since $\overline{\mathfrak{A}} \sim \mathfrak{B}$ may be proved from $\mathfrak{A} \sim \overline{\mathfrak{B}}$.

THEOREM 34.

$$(x)\big(F(x) \to G(x)\big) \to \big((Ex)F(x) \to (Ex)G(x)\big).$$

Proof: From the sentential formula

$$(A \to B) \to (\overline{B} \to \overline{A}),$$

we obtain by substitution:

$$(F(x) \to G(x)) \to (\overline{G}(x) \to \overline{F}(x)),$$
$$(x)\{(F(x) \to G(x)) \to (\overline{G}(x) \to \overline{F}(x))\} \quad [\text{Rule } \gamma')].$$

From the last formula we obtain, using Theorem 31,

$$(x)\{F(x) \to G(x)\} \to (x)\{\overline{G}(x) \to \overline{F}(x)\}.$$

By using Theorem 31 once more, and Rule V, we obtain from this

$$(x)\big(F(x) \to G(x)\big) \to \big((x)\overline{G}(x) \to (x)\overline{F}(x)\big).$$

By using Theorem 6, $(x)\overline{G}(x) \to (x)\overline{F}(x)$ may here be transformed into $\overline{(x)}\overline{F}(x) \to \overline{(x)}\overline{G}(x)$. Since $\overline{(x)}\overline{F}(x) \sim (Ex)F(x)$ and $\overline{(x)}\overline{G}(x) \sim (Ex)G(x)$, the theorem follows.

To Theorem 34 corresponds the following rule: If $\mathfrak{A}(x) \to \mathfrak{B}(x)$ is a theorem, then $(Ex)\mathfrak{A}(x) \to (Ex)\mathfrak{B}(x)$ is also a theorem.

For, by Rule γ'), one obtains from $\mathfrak{A}(x) \to \mathfrak{B}(x)$:

$$(x)\big(\mathfrak{A}(x) \to \mathfrak{B}(x)\big),$$

and by application of Theorem 34, $(Ex)\mathfrak{A}(x) \to (Ex)\mathfrak{B}(x)$.

Just as Theorem 32 was obtained from Theorem 31, we obtain, from Theorem 34:

THEOREM 34'.

$$(x)\big(F(x) \sim G(x)\big) \to \big((Ex)F(x) \sim (Ex)G(x)\big).$$

THEOREM 35. $(x)\big(F(x) \to A\big) \sim \big((Ex)F(x) \to A\big).$

Proof: $(x)\big(F(x) \to A\big)$ is an abbreviation for $(x)\big(\overline{F}(x) \vee A\big)$. The formula

$$(x)\big(\overline{F}(x) \vee A\big) \sim (x)\overline{F}(x) \vee A$$

is a theorem, proved like Theorem 26.

$$(x)\overline{F}(x) \sim \overline{(Ex)}F(x),$$
$$(x)(\overline{F}(x) \vee A) \sim \overline{(Ex)}F(x) \vee A.$$

Using once more the abbreviation →, there follows Theorem 35.

THEOREM 36. $(Ex)(y)F(x, y) \rightarrow (y)(Ex)F(x, y)$.

This is the Transposition Theorem already mentioned, concerning which we have noted that its converse fails to hold.

Proof:

$$F(x, y) \rightarrow (Ez)F(z, y) \qquad \text{[substitution in}$$
$$\text{Axiom f), and Rule } \delta')\,],$$
$$(y)(F(x, y) \rightarrow (Ez)F(z, y)) \qquad \text{[Rule } \gamma')\,].$$

Using Theorem 31, we obtain:

$$(y)F(x, y) \rightarrow (y)(Ez)F(z, y),$$
$$(Ex)(y)F(x, y) \rightarrow (y)(Ex)F(x, y) \qquad \text{[by Rules}$$
$$\gamma) \text{ and } \delta)\,].$$

§ 7. The Rule of Substitution; Construction of the Contradictory of a Formula

Now that we have proved a series of universally valid formulas, we will discuss some general rules which are particularly important in any attempt to survey the entire system of universally valid formulas.

The first rule is an extension of Rule VI. This asserted that sentences which stand in a relation of mutual implication, and are thus equivalent, may be substituted for one another. We extend this substitution rule thus:

RULE X. *Let* $\mathfrak{A}(x, y, \ldots, u)$ *and* $\mathfrak{B}(x, y, \ldots, u)$ *designate any formulas which contain the free variables* $x, y, \ldots, u$, *but no others. Further, let* $\mathfrak{A}(x, y, \ldots, u) \sim \mathfrak{B}(x, y, \ldots, u)$ *be a theorem. If, now, we have a formula* $\mathfrak{C}$ *in which* $\mathfrak{A}(\ldots)$ *occurs as a constituent part one or more times, with any variables in place of* $x, y, \ldots, u$, *and if* $\mathfrak{D}$ *is a formula which results from* $\mathfrak{C}$ *by the replacement, in the sense of our Rule a3), of* $\mathfrak{A}(\ldots)$ *by* $\mathfrak{B}(\ldots)$ *at one or more of its occurrences, then* $\mathfrak{C} \sim \mathfrak{D}$ *is also a theorem.*

Since we already have Rule VI, it is sufficient to show that on both sides of the equivalence $\mathfrak{A}(x, y, \ldots, u) \sim \mathfrak{B}(x, y, \ldots, u)$ the same quantifiers may be prefixed to $\mathfrak{A}(x, y, \ldots, u)$ and $\mathfrak{B}(x, y, \ldots, u)$, so that, for example, one may write:

$$(Ex)\,(y)\,\mathfrak{A}(x, y, \ldots, u) \sim (Ex)\,(y)\,\mathfrak{B}(x, y, \ldots, u).$$

It suffices to prove this for one quantifier. We show, therefore, that:

$$(x)\,\mathfrak{A}(x, y, \ldots, u) \sim (x)\,\mathfrak{B}(x, y, \ldots, u)$$

and

$$(Ex)\,\mathfrak{A}(x, y, \ldots, u) \sim (Ex)\,\mathfrak{B}(x, y, \ldots, u)$$

are theorems.

By Rule γ') we obtain from $\mathfrak{A}(x, y, \ldots, u) \sim \mathfrak{B}(x, y, \ldots, u)$:

$$(x)\,(\mathfrak{A}(x, y, \ldots, u) \sim \mathfrak{B}(x, y, \ldots, u)).$$

Using Theorem 32, we then obtain

$$(x)\,\mathfrak{A}(x, y, \ldots, u) \sim (x)\,\mathfrak{B}(x, y, , \ldots, u),$$

and likewise on the basis of Theorem 34' :

$$(Ex)\,\mathfrak{A}(x, y, \ldots, u) \sim (Ex)\,\mathfrak{B}(x, y, \ldots, u).$$

Another result of this kind is a rule for forming the contradictory of a formula.

RULE XI. *The contradictory of a formula in which the abbreviations* → *and* ∼ *do not occur is obtained by first replacing the universal quantifiers by existential quantifiers and conversely, then interchanging the signs* & *and* v, *and finally replacing the sentential and the predicate symbols by their negations.*

The proof of this rule is as follows:

For a formula not containing any universal and existential quantifiers, the theorem has already been proved in the sentential calculus. Now if we make use of this theorem and treat the combination of a universal quantifier and its scope as a single entity, we can always succeed in displacing the negation from the total expression to the outermost of its quantifiers. If there is a quantifier before the whole expression this is already the case. Now it follows from Theorem 33 that

$$\overline{(x)\,\mathfrak{A}(x)} \sim (Ex)\,\overline{\mathfrak{A}}(x),$$
$$\overline{(Ex)\,\mathfrak{A}(x)} \sim (x)\,\overline{\mathfrak{A}}(x).$$

Using these equivalences, the negation may be shifted from the quantifiers to the scopes. One now proceeds with these scopes in the same manner as with the total expression, until finally one arrives at the sentential or predicate symbols.

This method of transformation may be clarified by an example. Suppose our problem is to obtain for

$$\overline{(x)\,(Ey)\,(\overline{F}(x,y)\ \mathrm{v}\ (Ez)\,G(x,y,z))}$$

the expression which corresponds to the theorem. From Theorem 33 there follows first:

$$\overline{(x)}\,(Ey)\,(\overline{F}(x,y)\ \mathrm{v}\ (Ez)\,G(x,y,z)) \sim$$
$$(Ex)\,\overline{(Ey)}\,(\overline{F}(x,y)\ \mathrm{v}\ (Ez)\,G(x,y,z)),$$

and further there results the equivalent expression

$$(Ex)\,(y)\,\overline{\overline{F}(x,y)\ \mathrm{v}\ (Ez)\,G(x,y,z)}.$$

By using the special case of our theorem for the sentential calculus, and Rule X, we obtain:

$$(Ex)\,(y)\,(F(x,y)\ \&\ \overline{(Ez)}\,G(x,y,z))$$

and finally,

$$(Ex)\,(y)\,(F(x,y)\ \&\ (z)\,\overline{G}(x,y,z)).$$

This is precisely the expression corresponding to our rule.

§ 8. The Extended Principle of Duality; Normal Forms

From Rule XI of the preceding section a *Principle of Duality* may be proved, which we may regard as an extension of the Principle of Duality proved earlier for the sentential calculus. It reads as follows:

From a theorem which has the form of an implication or of an equivalence in whose components the signs → and ∼ do not occur, we get another theorem by replacing every universal quantifier by an existential quantifier in the same variable and vice versa, and by interchanging, in addition, the signs & and v. In the case of an implication, we must, in addition, change the order of the two components.

Proof: If $\mathfrak{A} \to \mathfrak{B}$ is a theorem, then so is $\overline{\mathfrak{B}} \to \overline{\mathfrak{A}}$, and if $\mathfrak{A} \sim \mathfrak{B}$ is a theorem then so is $\overline{\mathfrak{A}} \sim \overline{\mathfrak{B}}$. We now transform $\overline{\mathfrak{A}}$ and $\overline{\mathfrak{B}}$ by Rule XI of the preceding section. That is, we interchange the universal and the existential quantifiers as well as the symbols & and v, and replace the sentential and predicate symbols by their negations. However, since we are dealing in each case with a theorem, we may undo the last of these replacements by substituting their negations for the sentential and predicate variables in accordance with the Rule of Substitution.

The application of the extended Principle of Duality to theorems previously obtained supplies us at one stroke with a large number of universally valid formulas. The most important of these follow.[1]

THEOREM 26′. $(Ex)(A \& F(x)) \sim A \& (Ex)F(x)$.

THEOREM 28′. $(Ex)(A \text{ v } F(x)) \sim A \text{ v } (Ex)F(x)$.

THEOREM 29′. $(Ex)(Ey)F(x, y) \sim (Ey)(Ex)F(x, y)$.

THEOREM 30′.

$$(Ex)(F(x) \text{ v } G(x)) \sim (Ex)F(x) \text{ v } (Ex)G(x).$$

Theorems 29 and 29′ in combination with Rule X yield a further rule.

RULE XII. *A formula is transformed into an equivalent one by any rearrangement of two or more consecutive universal quan-*

---

[1] The numbering of the theorems is such as to indicate from which of the already proved universally valid formulas each is obtained by the Principle of Duality.

tifiers having the same scope. The corresponding rule for existential quantifiers also holds.

In the treatment of the sentential calculus it proved possible to reduce all sentential combinations to a standard normal form. We were able to express a sentential combination either as a conjunction of simple disjunctions or as a disjunction of simple conjunctions.

A certain *normal form* also exists for the predicate calculus. *In fact, any expression may be replaced by one in which all quantifiers occur un-negated at the beginning and are not separated by parentheses, so that their scopes all extend to the end of the formula.*[1] This normal form is usually called the *"prenex normal form."*

The advantage of this normal form consists in the fact that the expression after the quantifiers (the *"matrix"*) may be treated just like a sentential combination. The transformation into normal form is effected thus:

We first replace the abbreviations $\rightarrow$ and $\sim$ in the expression under consideration by their meanings. By repeated applications of Rule XI of the preceding section, we can easily arrive at a formula in which the negation bar stands only over the sentential and predicate variables. We now rewrite the bound variables in such a way that all quantifiers have different variables. Thus, instead of

$$(x)F(x) \text{ v } (x)G(x),$$

we write

$$(x)F(x) \text{ v } (y)G(y),$$

and so forth.

From the logical expression thus obtained we now get the normal form by placing all the quantifiers at the beginning of the formula in the order in which they occur and leaving everything else unaltered. The scopes of all the quantifiers then extend to the end of the formula.

---

[1] Just as in the sentential calculus, this mode of expression is by no means unique.

That the last transformation is actually permissible may be established in the following manner. Let the validity of the transformation be already proved for any expression containing fewer quantifiers than the one under consideration. This assertion says nothing in particular if no quantifier occurs. If the whole expression is the scope of a quantifier, the validity of the transformation is evident; in this case we need only make the transformation for the scope of the quantifier, and the scope contains fewer quantifiers. Otherwise, we consider the first quantifier of our expression. This is not itself in the scope of another quantifier. By applying the theorems:

$$A \vee (x) F(x) \sim (x) (A \vee F(x)),$$
$$(x) F(x) \vee A \sim (x) (F(x) \vee A),$$
$$A \& (x) F(x) \sim (x) (A \& F(x)),$$
$$(x) F(x) \& A \sim (x) (F(x) \& A)$$

or the corresponding theorems for the existential quantifier, we can shift this quantifier to the beginning of the formula and extend its scope over the entire formula. This brings us back to the preceding case, and the validity of the transformation is thereby proved in general.

The prenex normal form offers the advantage that, in general investigations in the predicate calculus, the range of the formulas to be considered can be considerably restricted. Nevertheless, the possibilities for the arrangement of the combination of quantifiers at the beginning of the formula—we shall call the combinations the "*prefix*" of the formula—are still so numerous as to be confusing. In this connection, a result of T. Skolem[1] is of interest, since it represents a certain strengthening of the theorems concerning the prenex normal form. This theorem of Skolem (in the formulation which we employ here) asserts the following:

For each formula of the predicate calculus, one can construct another, which not only is in prenex normal form, but also is such

---

[1] T. Skolem, *Logisch-kombinatorische Untersuchungen über die Erfüllbarkeit oder Beweisbarkeit mathematischer Sätze nebst einem Theoreme über dichte Mengen*, Vid. Skrifter I, Mat.-nat. Klasse 1920, No. 4.

that all its existential quantifiers precede all its universal quantifiers, and furthermore such that either both or neither of the
formulas are provable in our axiom system of the predicate
calculus.

In the following, a formula in prenex normal form in which
no existential quantifier follows any universal quantifier, will
be called a formula in Skolem normal form. In the proof of the
theorem, we need consider only formulas in prenex normal form.
Further, we can assume that the formula contains no free individual variables. For if such should occur, it is sufficient [by
Axiom e) and Rule γ')] to consider the formula obtained from
the given one by adding at the beginning of the formula the
universal quantifiers corresponding to the free individual variables. By the degree of such a formula, we understand the number of universal quantifiers to the right of which there occurs at
least one existential quantifier. It is then sufficient to show that
for each formula in prenex normal form but not in Skolem normal
form one can find a formula of lower degree which is provable if
and only if the former is provable. We may further assume that
the prefix of the formula in question begins with an existential
quantifier. For if the formula, which we will designate by $\mathfrak{A}$,
begins with a universal quantifier, then we take an individual
variable not occurring in $\mathfrak{A}$, say u, and similarly a predicate
variable, say G, and replace $\mathfrak{A}$ by the formula

$$(Eu)\,(\mathfrak{A}\,\&\,G(u)\,\mathrm{v}\,\overline{G}(u)),$$

which, as is easy to see, is provable if and only if $\mathfrak{A}$ is provable,
since we have conjoined a logically true formula with $\mathfrak{A}$ inside
the scope of (Eu). The formula $(Eu)\,(\mathfrak{A}\,\&\,G(u)\,\mathrm{v}\,\overline{G}(u))$ can
then be brought into prenex normal form in such a way that the
prefix begins with an existential quantifier.

Our formula thus begins with n $(n \geqq 1)$ existential quantifiers which are followed by at least one universal quantifier.
Consequently, it has the form

(I) $\qquad (Ex_1)\ldots(Ex_n)\,(y)\,\mathfrak{B}(x_1, x_2, \ldots, x_n, y)$.

$\mathfrak{B}(x_1, x_2, \ldots, x_n, y)$ here is a formula in prenex normal form
having only $x_1, x_2, \ldots, x_n, y$ as free individual variables. Let H

be a predicate variable with $n + 1$ argument places which does not occur in $\mathfrak{B}$. We construct the formula

(II) $(Ex_1) \ldots (Ex_n) [(Ey) (\mathfrak{B}(x_1, \ldots, x_n', y) \&$
$\overline{H}(x_1, \ldots, x_n, y)) \vee (z) H(x_1, \ldots, x_n, z)].$

This formula is provable if (I) is provable, and conversely. In fact, if we replace H by $\mathfrak{B}$ in (II) by Rule $a3$), we obtain

$(Ex_1) \ldots (Ex_n) [(Ey) (\mathfrak{B}(x_1, \ldots, x_n, y) \&$
$\overline{\mathfrak{B}}(x_1, \ldots, x_n, y)) \vee (z) \mathfrak{B}(x_1, \ldots, x_n, z)].$

We can then omit the part

$$(Ey) (\mathfrak{B}(x_1, \ldots, x_n, y) \& \overline{\mathfrak{B}}(x_1, \ldots, x_n, y)),$$

which represents a false sentence.

To obtain (II) from (I) is somewhat more complicated. First, from Theorem 31, we obtain by rewriting the bound variables:

$$(y) (F(y) \to G(y)) \to ((y) F(y) \to (y) G(y)).$$

Now, by Rule VII of the sentential calculus, we can transform a formula

$$\mathfrak{A} \to (\mathfrak{B} \to \mathfrak{C})$$

into

$$\mathfrak{B} \to \overline{\mathfrak{A}} \vee \mathfrak{C}.$$

In the present case this gives

$$(y) F(y) \to (Ey) (F(y) \& \overline{G}(y)) \vee (y) G(y),$$

provided that, in addition to using Rule XI for forming the contradictory, we also recall that $\mathfrak{A} \to \mathfrak{B}$ is an abbreviation for $\overline{\mathfrak{A}} \vee \mathfrak{B}$. If in this formula $F(y)$ is replaced by $\mathfrak{B}(x_1, \ldots, x_n, y)$, and $G(y)$ by $H(x_1, \ldots, x_n, y)$, we obtain

$(y) \mathfrak{B}(x_1, \ldots, x_n, y) \to (Ey) (\mathfrak{B}(x_1, \ldots, x_n, y) \&$
$\overline{H}(x_1, \ldots, x_n, y)) \vee (y) H(x_1, \ldots, x_n, y).$

By repeated application of the rule at the end of the proof for Theorem 34, we obtain further

$(Ex_1) \ldots (Ex_n) (y) \mathfrak{B}(x_1, \ldots, x_n, y)$
$\to (Ex_1) \ldots (Ex_n) [(Ey) (\mathfrak{B}(x_1, \ldots, x_n, y) \&$
$\overline{H}(x_1, \ldots, x_n, y)) \vee (y) H(x_1, \ldots, x_n, y)].$

If we take into account that (I) is by hypothesis provable, then the Rule of Implication and the Rule δ) for Rewriting Bound Variables give formula (II).

We now bring formula (II) into prenex normal form. This can be done in such a way that the prefix starts with

$$(Ex_1) \ldots (Ex_n)(Ey),$$

continues with the universal and existential quantifiers of $\mathfrak{B}(x_1, \ldots, x_n, y)$, and ends with the universal quantifier (z). Since the degree of the resulting formula is lower by one than the degree of (I), the theorem about the Skolem normal form is proved.

This theorem may be extended to assert not only that a formula and its Skolem normal form are either both provable or both not provable in the axiom system of the predicate calculus, but also that they are either both valid or both not valid. In order to do this we need only first verify that all the axioms of the predicate calculus are valid and that the rules of inference preserve validity, and then construct a proof exactly parallel to the foregoing one, but with assertions of provability replaced throughout by the corresponding assertions of validity.

§ 9. Consistency and Independence of the System of Axioms

The method of arithmetical interpretation, by means of which we were previously able to gain an insight into the consistency and independence of Axioms a) through d), also makes it possible for us to recognize that the entire *axiom system of the predicate calculus is consistent,* in the sense explained above. For this purpose, we must extend the arithmetical interpretation, which in the previous case applied only to sentential variables, to the symbols which have not yet been interpreted. This is done as follows:

We treat the predicate symbols in the same way as the sentential symbols. We regard both as arithmetical variables which can take the values 0 and 1 and no others. In this, we do not need to take account of how the argument places in the predicate symbols are filled. The quantifiers are everywhere omitted. The connective v will again be treated as indicating an arithmetical product, and by $\overline{0}$ we shall understand 1; by $\overline{1}$, 0.

With these conventions we again find, to begin with, that all the axioms, including e) and f), always yield the value 0 in the arithmetical interpretation. Furthermore, if one or more formulas always have the value 0, it is easily seen that any other formula obtained from them by means of our rules likewise always gives the value 0. Since, on the other hand, two expressions of which one is the negation of the other can not both be always 0, it follows that among the theorems which are obtainable from our axioms,no two can be contradictories of one another. Thus the condition of consistency is satisfied.

We must not, by the way, overestimate the significance of this consistency proof. It amounts to saying that we assume the domain of individuals underlying the axioms to consist of only a single element, and thus to be finite. We have absolutely no assurance that the formal introduction of postulates unobjectionable as regards content leaves the system of theorems consistent. For example, the question remains unanswered whether the addition of mathematical axioms would not, in our calculus, make any arbitrary formula provable. This problem, whose solution is of fundamental importance for mathematics, is incomparably more difficult than the question dealt with here. The mathematical axioms actually assume an infinite domain of individuals, and there are connected with the concept of infinity the difficulties and paradoxes which play a role in the discussion of the foundations of mathematics. In order to attack the latter problem successfully, D. Hilbert found it necessary to set up a special theory. To enter upon this theory, which of course uses the results of mathematical logic, is not possible within the limits of this book. The reader is referred, once and for all, to the book by Hilbert and Bernays.[1]

Let us now return to our system of axioms. We wish to prove the *independence of the system of axioms,* by showing that none

---

[1] D. Hilbert and P. Bernays, *Grundlagen der Mathematik* I, II (Berlin 1934, 1939).

of the Axioms a) through f), as well as none of the Rules α1) through α3), β), γ) and δ) is dispensable in obtaining the universally valid formulas of the predicate calculus.[1] In the following proofs of independence, the consistency of the calculus, which has just been proved, will be used.

First of all, we show that none of Axioms a) through d) is superfluous, and that it is therefore not possible to obtain any one of these axioms from the others by means of the rules of inference. In this we employ the fact proved above (Chap. I, § 13) that in the pure sentential calculus none of these axioms is dispensable; and, indeed, not even if we add to them $X \rightarrow X$, i.e. $\overline{X} \vee X$, as a further axiom.

Let us assume we had a proof, by means of the remaining axioms and the rules of inference of the predicate calculus, of any specific one of Axioms a) through d). We then remove the predicate and individual variables from the formulas of this proof in the following way. The universal and existential quantifiers are dropped out. Each predicate variable with arguments is replaced by the sentential variable X. This change transforms e) and f) into the formula $X \rightarrow X$.

In addition, the proof remains a proof after the transformation. A substitution in accordance with Rules α1) through α3) becomes either a substitution of the sentential calculus or a mere repetition. Formulas connected by the Rule of Implication remain so connected. Rule γ) and the Rule δ) of Rewriting now give a mere repetition.

Thus we would have a proof of the formula in question from the remaining ones of Axioms a) through d) and from $X \rightarrow X$, using the rules of the sentential calculus, in contradiction to the results obtained earlier.

We can show the independence of Axiom e) by proving that all formulas which can be proved without the use of this axiom

---

[1] A proof of independence has been given by McKinsey. Cf. J. C. C. McKinsey, *On the independence of Hilbert and Ackermann's postulates for the calculus of propositional functions*, Amer. J. of Math. Vol. 58, 1936. Simpler (unpublished) proofs have been communicated to us by P. Bernays and Arnold Schmidt. The text reproduces Bernays' train of thought.

have a characteristic property which this axiom lacks. In fact, if we change the formulas, beginning with the innermost scope, by replacing each part of the form $(x)\mathfrak{A}(x)$, $(y)\mathfrak{A}(y)$, etc., with $(x)\mathfrak{A}(x) \vee X \vee \overline{X}$, $(y)\mathfrak{A}(y) \vee X \vee \overline{X}$, etc., then each formula obtainable without the use of Axiom e) is transformed into a provable formula of the predicate calculus. For, Axioms a) through d) and Axiom f) are not affected by being subjected to the above transformation. Formulas connected by the Rule of Substitution a), the Rule of Implication, Rule $\gamma 2$), and Rule δ), remain so connected. In Rule $\gamma 1$), the final formula $\mathfrak{A} \rightarrow (x)\mathfrak{B}(x)$ is transformed into a formula of the form $\mathfrak{A}' \rightarrow (x)\mathfrak{B}'(x) \vee X \vee \overline{X}$, which is a provable formula. On the other hand, $(x)F(x) \rightarrow F(y)$ is transformed into $(x)F(x) \vee X \vee \overline{X} \rightarrow F(y)$, which is certainly not provable since the truth of the left hand side of the implication yields $F(y)$, and further, by substitution in accordance with Rule $a3$), would also yield $\overline{F}(y)$, which is a contradiction.

The independence of f)[1] can be shown in a quite similar way. Instead of replacing the partial formulas $(x)\mathfrak{A}(x)$ by $(x)\mathfrak{A}(x) \vee X \vee \overline{X}$, we replace $(Ex)\mathfrak{A}(x)$ by $(Ex)\mathfrak{A}(x) \& X \& \overline{X}$. Otherwise the considerations are the same.

By the same method, one can also show the independence of the two rules $\gamma 1$) and $\gamma 2$). In this case, if in the formulas we replace $(x)\mathfrak{A}(x)$ by $(x)\mathfrak{A}(x) \& X \& \overline{X}$, then all the formulas which can be obtained in the predicate calculus without employing $\gamma 1$) are again transformed into provable formulas. The formula $(x)(F(x) \vee \overline{F}(x))$, on the other hand, which is provable from the whole axiom system, is transformed into

$$(x) \left(F(x) \vee \overline{F}(x) \right) \& X \& \overline{X},$$

which is certainly not a provable formula. The independence of Rule $\gamma 1$) is thereby established. Likewise, the replacement of $(Ex)\mathfrak{A}(x)$ in the formulas by $(Ex)\mathfrak{A}(x) \vee X \vee \overline{X}$ establishes the independence of Rule $\gamma 2$), since the formula $\overline{(Ex)} \left(F(x) \& \overline{F}(x) \right)$

---

[1] The fact that the existential quantifier can, strictly speaking, be dispensed with in the axiom system has evidently nothing to do with the independence of Axiom f), since $(Ex)\mathfrak{A}(x)$ can, after all, be considered to be an abbreviation for $\overline{(x)}\overline{\mathfrak{A}}(x)$ (cf. p. 59).

is transformed by this substitution into a formula which is not provable.

The independence of Rule α1) is established by the fact that of the formulas in which individual variables occur only those are provable without this rule which have one of the following forms:

$$(x)\,\mathfrak{A}(x) \to \mathfrak{A}(y)\,; \quad \mathfrak{A}(y) \to (Ex)\,\mathfrak{A}(x)\,;$$
$$(x)\,\mathfrak{A}(x) \to (x)\,\mathfrak{A}(x)\,; \quad (Ex)\,\mathfrak{A}(x) \to (Ex)\,\mathfrak{A}(x)\,;$$
$$(Ez)\,((x)\,\mathfrak{A}(x) \to \mathfrak{A}(z))\,; \quad (Ez)\,(\mathfrak{A}(z) \to (Ex)\,\mathfrak{A}(x))\,,$$

or which are obtainable from such formulas by substitution for the individual variables, or by rewriting the bound variables. For, Axioms e) and f) have this form, and by the rules of inference we always obtain only formulas of this kind. Thus, for example, formula $(x)\,F(x) \to (Ex)\,F(x)$ is not provable without the use of α1).

The independence of Rule α2) is established by the following transformation. In all formulas we omit those argument places of the predicate variables which are occupied by the free individual variable z. For example, $F(x, z)$ is transformed into $F(x)$, $G(z)$ into G. Under this transformation, a proof which did not use the Rule of Substitution for individual variables once more goes into a proof. Since the axioms are not altered by the transformation, any formula provable without the use of α2) is again transformed into a provable formula. However, the provable formula $(x)\,F(x) \to F(z)$ is transformed into the formula $(x)\,F(x) \to F$, which is certainly not a provable formula. (Here the second F is a sentential variable.)

In a corresponding manner, we prove the independence of the Rule δ) for Rewriting Bound Variables. We modify the above transformation, which was applicable to the free individual variable z, so that it now applies to the bound individual variable z. Thus we must also omit the symbols (z) and (Ez). Here, too, a formula which is provable without the use of the Rule δ) is again transformed into a provable formula. The formula $(z)\,F(z) \to F(x)$, on the other hand, which is certainly provable, is transformed into $F \rightarrow F(x)$, which is certainly not a provable formula.

In order to establish the independence of Rule $a3$), we replace any partial formula $(x)\mathfrak{A}(x)$, $(y)\mathfrak{A}(y)$, etc., containing the predicate variable G, by $(x)\mathfrak{A}(x) \vee X \vee \overline{X}$, $(y)\mathfrak{A}(y) \vee X \vee \overline{X}$, etc. Then any formula provable without the use of Rule $a3$) is transformed into a provable formula. On the other hand, the formula $(x)G(x) \rightarrow G(y)$ is transformed into one which is certainly not provable.

The indispensability of the Rule of Implication is established by the fact that without this rule, only formulas of the form $\overline{\mathfrak{A}} \vee \mathfrak{B}$ can be proved. For, all the axioms have this form, and the rules (with the exception of β)) preserve this form. For example, the formula $X \vee \overline{X}$ is not provable without the use of Rule β).

§ 10. The Completeness of the Axiom System

We remarked in the first chapter (§ 13) that the completeness of an axiom system can be defined in two ways. In the stronger sense of the word, completeness means that the addition of a previously unprovable formula to the axiom system always yields a contradiction. We do not have this kind of completeness here. In order to establish the incompleteness of the system of axioms, we need only find a formula which, in the arithmetical interpretation (used in the proof of consistency), is identically 0, but is not a consequence of the axioms. Such a formula is

$$(Ex)F(x) \rightarrow (x)F(x).$$

That this formula does not follow from the axioms can be made plausible by considering the assertion which it stands for: "If there is an x for which $F(x)$ holds, then $F(x)$ is true for all x," which is certainly not universally valid. In fact, it is not valid for an arbitrary predicate F if the domain of individuals contains more than one element.

The strictly formal proof for the impossibility of proving the formula from the axioms proceeds as follows:

We first give a method for changing logical formulas into such formulas as contain only sentential variables. First we remove the free variables which occur in a formula by placing in front of the formula the universal quantifiers belonging to these free variables. Proceeding from the outside, we then remove the quantifiers by substituting

$$\mathfrak{A}(1) \ \& \ \mathfrak{A}(2) \quad \text{for} \quad (x)\mathfrak{A}(x),$$
$$\mathfrak{A}(1) \ v \ \mathfrak{A}(2) \quad \text{for} \quad (Ex)\mathfrak{A}(x).[1]$$

Our formulas now contain, besides sentential variables, sentences of the form $F(1)$, $F(2)$, $G(1,2)$, ...

All of these different sentences we now replace by (different) sentential variables.

We now assert that, under this transformation, any formula provable from the axioms goes over into a logically true sentential combination.

We first show this for the axioms. This is clear for Axioms a) through d), since they are unaltered by the transformation. The axiom $(x)F(x) \to F(y)$ is transformed thus:

$$(y)\,((x)F(x) \to F(y)),$$
$$((x)F(x) \to F(1)) \ \& \ ((x)F(x) \to F(2)),$$
$$(F(1) \ \& \ F(2) \to F(1)) \ \& \ (F(1) \ \& \ F(2) \to F(2)),$$
$$(A \ \& \ B \to A) \ \& \ (A \ \& \ B \to B).$$

The last is indeed a logically true sentential combination.

Analogously, we have for the axiom

$$F(y) \to (Ex)F(x)$$

the transformations

$$(y)\,(F(y) \to (Ex)F(x)),$$
$$(F(1) \to (Ex)F(x)) \ \& \ (F(2) \to (Ex)F(x)),$$
$$(F(1) \to F(1) \ v \ F(2)) \ \& \ (F(2) \to F(1) \ v \ F(2)),$$
$$(A \to A \ v \ B) \ \& \ (B \to A \ v \ B),$$

which likewise lead to a logically true formula. We now need only show that the application of Rules $a)$, $\beta)$, $\gamma)$, and $\delta)$ leaves this property unaltered.

---

[1] "1" and "2" are here proper names of individuals. Thus our elimination of the quantifiers actually amounts to assuming that the domain of individuals contains only the two elements 1 and 2.

If we have two formulas of which the second results from the first by application of Rules α1) or α3), then, after the transformation, either the two formulas are connected by the Rule of Substitution of the sentential calculus, or else the second formula is a conjunction of formulas each one of which is deducible from the first by means of the Rule of Substitution of the sentential calculus. Rules α2) and δ) give rise to mere repetitions. The Rule of Implication retains its form, provided no free individual variables occur in the formulas. If the Rule of Implication also contains free individual variables, then it may indeed alter its form upon prefixing the universal quantifiers. For example,

$$\frac{\mathfrak{A}(x)}{\mathfrak{A}(x) \to \mathfrak{B}(x)}{\mathfrak{B}(x)}$$

is changed into the new rule

$$\frac{(x)\,\mathfrak{A}(x)}{(x)\,(\mathfrak{A}(x) \to \mathfrak{B}(x))}{(x)\,\mathfrak{B}(x)}\,.$$

By eliminating the universal quantifiers, we then obtain

$$\frac{\mathfrak{A}(1)\,\&\,\mathfrak{A}(2)}{(\mathfrak{A}(1) \to \mathfrak{B}(1))\,\&\,(\mathfrak{A}(2) \to \mathfrak{B}(2))}{\mathfrak{B}(1)\,\&\,\mathfrak{B}(2)}\,.$$

But this rule also corresponds to the rules of the sentential calculus. The situation is similar in case several individual variables occur.

Finally, we come to γ). An expression

$$\mathfrak{A} \to \mathfrak{B}(x)$$

is transformed (provided $\mathfrak{A}$ contains no free variable) by our process into

$$(x)\,(\mathfrak{A} \to \mathfrak{B}(x)),$$
$$(\mathfrak{A} \to \mathfrak{B}(1))\,\&\,(\mathfrak{A} \to \mathfrak{B}(2)),$$

and so forth. $\mathfrak{A} \to (x)\mathfrak{B}(x)$ becomes:

$$\mathfrak{A} \to \mathfrak{B}(1) \,\&\, \mathfrak{B}(2).$$

According to the rules of the sentential calculus, however, the two formulas are equivalent. The situation is the same if $\mathfrak{A}$ contains free variables. A corresponding remark applies to that part of Rule γ) which is concerned with adding an existential quantifier.

We have thus indeed shown that any formula provable from the axioms goes over into a logically true sentential combination under our transformation. Now

$$(Ex)F(x) \to (x)F(x)$$

does not have this property, for it is transformed into

$$F(1) \,\mathrm{v}\, F(2) \to F(1) \,\&\, F(2),$$
$$A \,\mathrm{v}\, B \to A \,\&\, B,$$

and this is not a logically true sentential combination.

Having shown that the axiom system is not complete in the stronger sense of the word, we may ask whether we have completeness in the other sense, defined on page 42. The question here is whether all universally valid formulas of the predicate calculus, as defined at the beginning of § 5 of this chapter, can be proved in the axiom system. We actually do have completeness in this sense. The proof is due to K. Gödel,[1] whose exposition we shall follow.

As we saw in § 8, we can find, for any universally valid formula of the predicate calculus, a universally valid formula in Skolem normal form such that both formulas are provable or both not provable. We may therefore restrict ourselves to showing that all universally valid formulas in Skolem normal form are provable.

Let

$$(Ex_1) \dots (Ex_k)\,(y_1) \dots (y_l)\,\mathfrak{A}(x_1, \dots, x_k; y_1, \dots, y_l)$$

be such a formula.

---

[1] K. Gödel, *Die Vollständigkeit der Axiome des logischen Funktionenkalküls*. Mh. Math. Physik Vol. 37 (1930).

We note, first of all, that we can enumerate all the k-tuples $(x_{i_1}, x_{i_2}, \ldots, x_{i_k})$ formed from the infinite sequence of individual variables $x_0, x_1, x_2, \ldots$ by ordering them in the standard way, first according to increasing index sums $(i_1 + i_2 + \ldots + i_k)$, and then lexicographically within each group having the same index sum. Thus the sequence begins with $(x_0, x_0, \ldots, x_0)$; $(x_0, x_0, \ldots, x_1)$; $(x_0, x_0, \ldots, x_1, x_0)$; .... Let the n-th of these k-tuples be $(x_{n_1}, x_{n_2}, \ldots, x_{n_k})$. Further, let $\mathfrak{B}_n$ stand for the formula

$$\mathfrak{A}(\ x_{n_1}, x_{n_2}, \ldots, x_{n_k}\ ;\ x_{(n-1)l+1}, x_{(n-1)l+2}, \ldots, x_{nl}).$$

We note that the individual variables after the semicolon are different from those before it, as well as from all variables occurring in any formula $\mathfrak{B}_p (p < n)$. On the other hand, all of the variables $x_{n_1}, \ldots, x_{n_k}$ already occur in some of the formulas $\mathfrak{B}_p (p < n)$. Further, we let $\mathfrak{C}_n$ stand for the disjunction $\mathfrak{B}_1 \vee \mathfrak{B}_2 \vee \ldots \vee \mathfrak{B}_n$; and $\mathfrak{D}_n$ for the formula that arises from $\mathfrak{C}_n$ by prefixing to $\mathfrak{C}_n$ all the universal quantifiers belonging to the free individual variables. We now associate with each formula $\mathfrak{C}_n$ a formula of the sentential calculus, as follows: All the elementary components of this formula, which (apart from sentential variables) are predicate variables with individual variables as arguments, are replaced by sentential variables, in such a way that a given component is everywhere replaced by the same sentential variable and different components are replaced by different sentential variables. The sentential formula thus associated with $\mathfrak{C}_n$ will be called $\mathfrak{E}_n$. Clearly, $\mathfrak{E}_n$ is such that $\mathfrak{C}_n$ may be obtained from $\mathfrak{E}_n$ by the Rule of Substitution $a1$).

We now have the following alternatives:

1. There is an n such that $\mathfrak{E}_n$ is a logically true formula of the sentential calculus.

2. There is no n such that $\mathfrak{E}_n$ is a logically true formula of the sentential calculus.

We shall prove the following:

(A). In case 1, the formula

$$(Ex_1) \ldots (Ex_k)(y_1) \ldots (y_l) \mathfrak{A}(x_1, \ldots, x_k; y_1, \ldots, y_l)$$

is provable in the axiom system of the predicate calculus.

(B). In case 2, the above formula is not a universally valid formula, because in the domain of individuals constituted by the natural numbers there can be found predicates which, when substituted for the predicate variables of the formula, turn it into a false sentence.

From these results, which still remain to be proved, we have as conclusions:

Any universally valid formula of the predicate calculus is provable; i.e., our axiom system consisting of primitive formulas a) *through* f) *and Rules* α1) *through* α3), β), γ), *and* δ), *has the property of completeness.*

Let a formula be valid in the domain of natural numbers (or in any other denumerably infinite domain) as its domain of reference for individual variables, i.e., let the formula go over into a true sentence when any substitution of number-theoretic predicate constants is made for its predicate variables and of definite numerals (or other names of numbers) for its free individual variables. Then it is valid in any domain of individuals.

The latter important theorem, which here follows as a corollary from our proof, can be given a simpler independent proof, and was first obtained by L. Löwenheim.[1]

We now must prove assertions (A) and (B). First let us prove (A). For some n, let $\mathfrak{C}_n$ be a logically true sentential formula. Since one obtains $\mathfrak{C}_n$ from $\mathfrak{C}_n$ by substitution in accordance with Rule α1) and, further, $\mathfrak{D}_n$ from $\mathfrak{C}_n$ by application of Rule γ'), it suffices to show that, for every n,

$$\mathfrak{D}_n \to (Ex_1) \ldots (Ex_k)(y_1) \ldots (y_l)\mathfrak{A}(x_1, \ldots, x_k; y_1, \ldots, y_l)$$

is a theorem of the predicate calculus. This can be shown by induction on n. $\mathfrak{D}_1$ has the form

$$(x_0)(x_1) \ldots (x_l)\mathfrak{A}(x_0, \ldots, x_0; x_1, \ldots, x_l).$$
$$(y_1) \ldots (y_l)\mathfrak{A}(z_1, \ldots, z_k; y_1, \ldots, y_l) \to$$
$$(Ex_1) \ldots (Ex_k)(y_1) \ldots (y_l)\mathfrak{A}(x_1, \ldots, x_k; y_1, \ldots, y_l)$$

---

[1] L. Löwenheim, *Über Möglichkeiten im Relativkalkül,* Math. Ann. Vol. 76 (1915). The work of T. Skolem, cited at the end of § 8 of this chapter, contains a considerable simplification of the method of proof.

can be proved by repeated applications of Axiom f) and Rule V. There follows from this, by substitution,

$$(y_1) \ldots (y_l) \mathfrak{A}(z_0, \ldots, z_0; y_1, \ldots, y_l) \rightarrow$$
$$(Ex_1) \ldots (Ex_k)(y_1) \ldots (y_l) \mathfrak{A}(x_1, \ldots, x_k; y_1, \ldots, y_l).$$

Further, by Axiom e) and Rule δ),

$$\mathfrak{D}_1 \rightarrow (y_1) \ldots (y_l) \mathfrak{A}(z_0, \ldots, z_0; y_1, \ldots, y_l).$$

Hence by Rule V,

$$\mathfrak{D}_1 \rightarrow (Ex_1) \ldots (Ex_k)(y_1) \ldots (y_l) \mathfrak{A}(x_1, \ldots, x_k; y_1, \ldots, y_l).$$

This formula is the case $n = 1$ of the proof by induction. Now assume, as hypothesis of induction,

$$\mathfrak{D}_{n-1} \rightarrow (Ex_1) \ldots (Ex_k)(y_1) \ldots (y_l) \mathfrak{A}(x_1, \ldots, x_k; y_1, \ldots, y_l).$$

By definition, $\mathfrak{D}_n$ has the form

$$(x_0)(x_1) \ldots (x_{nl}) \mathfrak{C}_n; \ i.e. \ (x_0)(x_1) \ldots (x_{nl}) (\mathfrak{C}_{n-1} \vee \mathfrak{B}_n),$$

where $\mathfrak{B}_n$ is

$$\mathfrak{A}(x_{n_1}, \ldots, x_{n_k}; x_{(n-1)l+1}, \ldots, x_{nl}).$$

Since, as noted above, the variables $x_{(n-1)l+1}, \ldots, x_{nl}$ do not occur in $\mathfrak{C}_{n-1}$, we obtain by Theorem 26:

$$(x_{(n-1)l+1}) \ldots (x_{nl}) (\mathfrak{C}_{n-1} \vee \mathfrak{B}_n) \sim \mathfrak{C}_{n-1} \vee (x_{(n-1)l+1}) \ldots (x_{nl}) \mathfrak{B}_n.$$

Then by means of the sentential calculus (which enables us to transform an equivalence sentence into a conjunction of implications, and then assert either implication separately) and by means, further, of Rule γ'), Theorem 31, and Rule δ), we obtain as a theorem:

$$\mathfrak{D}_n \rightarrow (x_0)(x_1) \ldots (x_{(n-1)l})$$
$$[\mathfrak{C}_{n-1} \vee (y_1) \ldots (y_l) \mathfrak{A}(x_{n_1}, \ldots, x_{n_k}; y_1, \ldots, y_l)].$$

Hence by repeated application of Rule δ) we have:

$$\mathfrak{D}_n \rightarrow (z_0)(z_1) \ldots (z_{(n-1)l})$$
$$[\mathfrak{C}'_{n-1} \vee (y_1) \ldots (y_l) \mathfrak{A}(z_{n_1}, \ldots, z_{n_k}; y_1, \ldots, y_l)].$$

where $\mathfrak{C}'_{n-1}$ is the result of substituting z_i for every x_i in $\mathfrak{C}_{n-1}$.

Now reverting to the formula

$$(y_1) \ldots (y_l)\, \mathfrak{A}(z_1, \ldots, z_k; y_1, \ldots, y_l) \rightarrow$$
$$(Ex_1) \ldots (Ex_k)\, (y_1) \ldots (y_l)\, \mathfrak{A}(x_1, \ldots, x_k; y_1, \ldots, y_l),$$

obtained above, we have by Rule $a2$) and Rule IV:

$$\mathfrak{C}'_{n-1}\ \mathrm{v}\ (y_1) \ldots (y_l)\, \mathfrak{A}(z_{n1}, \ldots, z_{nk}; y_1, \ldots, y_l) \rightarrow$$
$$\mathfrak{C}'_{n-1}\ \mathrm{v}\ (Ex_1) \ldots (Ex_k)\, (y_1) \ldots (y_l)\, \mathfrak{A}(x_1, \ldots, x_k; y_1, \ldots, y_l)$$

Hence by several applications of Rule γ') and Theorem 31,

$$(z_0)\, (z_1) \ldots (z_{(n-1)l})$$
$$[\,\mathfrak{C}'_{n-1}\ \mathrm{v}\ (y_1) \ldots (y_l)\, \mathfrak{A}(z_{n1}, \ldots, z_{nk}; y_1, \ldots, y_l)\,]$$
$$\rightarrow (z_0)\, (z_1) \ldots (z_{(n-1)l})$$
$$[\,\mathfrak{C}'_{n-1}\ \mathrm{v}\ (Ex_1) \ldots (Ex_k)\, (y_1) \ldots (y_l)\, \mathfrak{A}(x_1, \ldots, x_k; y_1, \ldots, y_l)\,].$$

Hence by Rule V,

$$\mathfrak{D}_n \rightarrow (z_0)\, (z_1) \ldots (z_{(n-1)l})$$
$$[\,\mathfrak{C}'_{n-1}\ \mathrm{v}\ (Ex_1) \ldots (Ex_k)\, (y_1) \ldots (y_l)\, \mathfrak{A}(x_1, \ldots, x_k; y_1, \ldots, y_l)\,].$$

From this we obtain by repeated use of Theorem 26, Rule X, and Rule δ) :

$$\mathfrak{D}_n \rightarrow (x_0)\, (x_1) \ldots (x_{(n-1)l})\, \mathfrak{C}_{n-1}\ \mathrm{v}\ (Ex_1) \ldots (Ex_k)\, (y_1) \ldots (y_l)$$
$$\mathfrak{A}(x_1, \ldots, x_k; y_1, \ldots, y_l),$$

i.e.

$$\mathfrak{D}_n \rightarrow \mathfrak{D}_{n-1}\ \mathrm{v}\ (Ex_1) \ldots (Ex_k)\, (y_1) \ldots (y_l)\, \mathfrak{A}(x_1, \ldots, x_k; y_1, \ldots, y_l).$$

Since we have assumed, as hypothesis of induction,

$$\mathfrak{D}_{n-1} \rightarrow (Ex_1) \ldots (Ex_k)\, (y_1) \ldots (y_l)\, \mathfrak{A}(x_1, \ldots, x_k; y_1, \ldots, y_l),$$

there easily follows by the sentential calculus

$$\mathfrak{D}_n \rightarrow (Ex_1) \ldots (Ex_k)\, (y_1) \ldots (y_l)\, \mathfrak{A}(x_1, \ldots, x_k; y_1, \ldots, y_l),$$

This completes the induction.

We turn now to the proof of (B). Let none of the $\mathfrak{E}_n$ be a logically true sentential formula. It is useful, in what follows, to give the sentential formulas $\mathfrak{E}_n$ a somewhat more special form. $\mathfrak{E}_n$ was obtained from $\mathfrak{C}_n$ by replacing with sentential variables those of the elementary components occurring in $\mathfrak{C}_n$ which consist of predicate variables with arguments from the sequence $x_0, x_1, x_2, \ldots$. We now agree to carry out this replacement by sentential variables by substituting F_0 for $F(x_0)$, F_1 for $F(x_1)$, $G_{1,2,3}$ for $G(x_1, x_2, x_3)$, etc. Now each formula $\mathfrak{E}_{n+1}$ contains all the sentential variables of $\mathfrak{E}_n$, and others in addition. We imagine the totality of sentential variables occurring in the $\mathfrak{E}_n$ to be in some way enumerated, so that it makes sense to speak of the first sentential variable, the second sentential variable, etc. We may, for example, enumerate them by first taking the sentential variables of $\mathfrak{E}_1$ in any definite order, then those which occur for the first time in $\mathfrak{E}_2$, and so on.

Now since no $\mathfrak{E}_n$ is a logically true sentential formula, the sentential variables occurring in an $\mathfrak{E}_n$ can be replaced by the truth values, truth and falsehood, in such a way that $\mathfrak{E}_n$ is transformed into a false sentence. Then, in conformity with the terminology used in the sentential calculus, we shall speak of a system of truth values which satisfy $\overline{\mathfrak{E}}_n$. For each $\overline{\mathfrak{E}}_n$ there is obviously only a finite number of different such systems; but altogether there are infinitely many, since systems corresponding to formulas $\overline{\mathfrak{E}}_n$ for different values of n are, of course, considered as different.

With each of the infinitely many sentential variables we now associate uniquely either the value truth or the value falsehood. If the first sentential variable is replaced in infinitely many of our truth-value systems by the value truth, then we assign to it the value truth; otherwise, the value falsehood. We now consider only those systems in which the first sentential variable has been replaced by the value just assigned to it. If the second sentential variable occurs in infinitely many of these with the value truth, then this value will be assigned to it; otherwise, the value falsehood. In the same way we determine the value for each succeeding sentential variable by considering each time only those value systems in which the preceding sentential variables have the values already determined.

If we now replace the sentential variables by the values assigned to them, then all the $\mathfrak{E}_n$ are simultaneously transformed into false sentences. We now define certain number-theoretic predicates, which will be substituted for the predicate variables occurring in $\mathfrak{A}(x_1, \ldots, x_k; y_1, \ldots, y_l)$. For example, if a predicate variable $F(\ ,\ ,\ )$ with three argument places occurs, then we have sentential variables F_{i_1, i_2, i_3} in the $\mathfrak{E}_n$. We now define the associated number-theoretic predicate Φ by the condition that $\Phi(p, q, r)$ shall have the truth-value assigned to $F_{p, q, r}$ for any triple of natural numbers p, q, and r. Thus with each predicate variable there is associated a number-theoretic predicate constant with the same number of argument places. If now in

$$(Ex_1) \ldots (Ex_k) (y_1) \ldots (y_l) \mathfrak{A}(x_1, \ldots, x_k; y_1, \ldots, y_l)$$

we take the natural numbers as the domain of individuals, and substitute for the predicate variables the number-theoretic predicates just defined, then it is easy to see that the formula is transformed into a false sentence, in other words, that

$$(x_1) \ldots (x_k) (Ey_1) \ldots (Ey_l) \overline{\mathfrak{A}}(x_1, \ldots, x_k; y_1, \ldots, y_l)$$

is transformed into a true sentence. For if we select, say, the n-th k-tuple of natural numbers, designated above by $(n_1, \ldots, n_k)$, then

$$\overline{\mathfrak{A}}(n_1, \ldots, n_k;\ (n-1)l + 1, \ldots, nl)$$

has, after replacement of the predicate variables, the opposite truth value to that of the last disjunct of $\mathfrak{E}_n$ in which the sentential variables have been replaced by their assigned truth values, i.e. it is true. Since the like holds for every k-tuple, it follows that

$$(x_1) \ldots (x_k) (Ey_1) \ldots (Ey_l) \overline{\mathfrak{A}}(x_1, \ldots, x_k; y_1, \ldots, y_l)$$

is true for the given domain of individuals. This completes the proof of (B).

§ 11. Derivation of Consequences from Given Premises; Relation to Universally Valid Formulas

So far we have used the predicate calculus only for deducing valid formulas. The premises in our deductions, viz. Axioms a) through f), were themselves of a purely logical nature. Now we shall illustrate by a few examples the general methods of formal derivation in the predicate calculus, which previously, before the axioms were set forth, could merely be sketched. It is now a question of deriving the consequences from any premises whatsoever, no longer of a purely logical nature.

In the premises not only variables will occur, but also *predicate constants* and *individual constants*. As symbols for predicate constants we use either a *combination of capitals followed by small letters such as Mt, Mn, Dsc*, etc., or *capital Greek letters*, and for mathematical predicates we use well-known predicate symbols from mathematics itself, such as $<$, $>$, $=$, etc. The concept of a formula, as introduced in § 4, is correspondingly extended.

Formal derivations are accomplished by writing out the premises of the derivations in symbols and adding them as primitive formulas (axioms) to the logical Axioms a)-f), and using them both as the basis for the formal operations to be carried out in accordance with the rules of inference a), β), γ), δ).

When interpreting the formulas as regards content, we must bear in mind that the individual variables no longer refer, in general, to a domain of individuals which is left indeterminate; rather, the latter is usually more or less definitely determined by the nature of the premises, so that the individual members of the domain may perhaps be the integers, the real numbers, the points in a plane, or any other things whatsoever. It is also possible that several domains of individuals come into consideration, as is the case in the second of the examples treated below. In this case we need several classes of individual variables. The predicate variables must then be differentiated according to the kind of arguments they have. We can then write out the Axioms e) and f) as many times as there are classes of objects considered. The resultant complication of the predicate calculus may, however, be avoided, since it is always possible (as we shall show in treating the second example below) to reduce the case of several domains of individuals to the case of a single domain.

We first give some simple examples.

As our first example, we may take a syllogism in which one of the premises is a singular judgment. A syllogism of this sort is furnished by the standard example:

"All men are mortal; Socrates is a man; therefore Socrates is mortal."

In this syllogism three constants occur. To the words "man" and "mortal" correspond two predicates $Mn(x)$ and $Mt(x)$, for which the common class of individuals may be considered to be that of living beings. The third constant is the proper name "Socrates." Written as formulas, the two premises are:

$$(x)\left(Mn(x) \to Mt(x)\right),$$
$$Mn(\text{Socrates}).$$

By substitution in the formula

$$(x)F(x) \to F(y),$$

we obtain

$$(x)\left(Mn(x) \to Mt(x)\right) \to \left(Mn(y) \to Mt(y)\right)$$

and further

$$(x)\left(Mn(x) \to Mt(x)\right) \to \left(Mn(\text{Socrates}) \to Mt(\text{Socrates})\right),$$
$$Mn(\text{Socrates}) \to Mt(\text{Socrates}) \qquad [\text{Rule } \beta)],$$
$$Mt(\text{Socrates}) \qquad [\text{Rule } \beta)].$$

The last formula, however, is the symbolic rendering of our conclusion "Socrates is mortal."

We shall now give in addition two examples of mathematical derivations. Let us first consider the following derivation from geometry.

Hypothesis: *"At most one straight line passes through two different points."*

Conclusion: *"Two different straight lines have not more than one point in common."*

The predicates occurring here are the following: First the relation $A(x, y)$: "x lies on y." Here the first argument place refers to the class of points; the second, to the class of straight lines. Further, there occurs the predicate of being different, that is, the opposite of the predicate of identity $\equiv (x, y)$. The argument places of this predicate may refer to points as well as to lines; of course, the assertion of the identity of a point with a line is always to be regarded as false. For the sake of clarity we shall use as arguments referring to points small italic letters, and as those referring to straight lines, capital italic letters.[1] Proper names of individuals do not occur. The symbolic expression for the hypothesis is:

$$(x)\,(y)\,\{\overline{\equiv}\,(x,y) \to \overline{(EG)}\,(EH)$$
$$[\equiv(G,H)\;\&\;\varLambda\,(x,G)\;\&\;\varLambda\,(x,H)\;\&\;\varLambda\,(y,G)\;\&\;\varLambda\,(y,H)\,]\,\};$$

The conclusion is written:

$$(G)\,(H)\,\{\overline{\equiv}\,(G,H) \to \overline{(Ex)}\,(Ey)$$
$$[\equiv(x,y)\;\&\;\varLambda\,(x,G)\;\&\;\varLambda\,(x,H)\;\&\;\varLambda\,(y,G)\;\&\;\varLambda\,(y,H)\,]\,\}.$$

If we write

$$\mathfrak{A}(x,y,G,H)$$

as an abbreviation for

$$\varLambda\,(x,G)\;\&\;\varLambda\,(y,G)\;\&\;\varLambda\,(x,H)\;\&\;\varLambda\,(y,H)$$

and make use of the definition of the symbol $\to$, then we obtain as symbolic renderings of the hypothesis and conclusion respectively:

$$(x)\,(y)\,\{\equiv(x,y)\;\text{v}\;\overline{(EG)}\,(EH)\,[\overline{\equiv}(G,H)\;\&\;\mathfrak{A}(x,y,G,H)\,]\,\}$$

and

$$(G)\,(H)\,\{\equiv(G,H)\;\text{v}\;\overline{(Ex)}\,(Ey)\,[\overline{\equiv}(x,y)\;\&\;\mathfrak{A}(x,y,G,H)\,]\,\}.$$

Using the rule given in § 8 for forming the negation of an expression, the two expressions may be transformed into

$$(x)\,(y)\,\{\equiv(x,y)\;\text{v}\;(G)\,(H)\,[\equiv(G,H)\;\text{v}\;\overline{\mathfrak{A}}(x,y,G,H)\,]\,\},$$
$$(G)\,(H)\,\{\equiv(G,H)\;\text{v}\;(x)\,(y)\,[\equiv(x,y)\;\text{v}\;\overline{\mathfrak{A}}(x,y,G,H)\,]\,\}.$$

We now reduce both expressions to normal form, and obtain:

$$(x)\,(y)\,(G)\,(H)\,\{\equiv(x,y)\;\text{v}\;(\equiv(G,H)\;\text{v}\;\overline{\mathfrak{A}}(x,y,G,H))\,\},$$
$$(G)\,(H)\,(x)\,(y)\,\{\equiv(G,H)\;\text{v}\;(\equiv(x,y)\;\text{v}\;\overline{\mathfrak{A}}(x,y,G,H))\,\}.$$

From these last expressions it is immediately clear that the conclusion may be derived from the hypothesis. For, the formula for the hypothesis goes over into the formula for the conclusion if the associative and commutative laws are applied to the products, and the Rule of Transposition is applied to the universal

---

[1] Confusion with sentential variables cannot occur here.

quantifiers. At the same time we recognize that conversely we may also infer the truth of the hypothesis from that of the conclusion.

The simultaneous treatment of two domains of individuals can be avoided in the following way, whose generalization to cover any case needs no particular explanation. We posit a single domain of individuals, consisting of the points and the straight lines, and introduce two predicate constants: $\Pi(x)$, *i.e.* "x is a point," and $\Gamma(x)$, *i.e.* "x is a straight line." The hypothesis in our example is then written as follows:

$$(x)\,(y)\,\{\,\big(\Pi(x)\,\&\,\Pi(y)\,\&\,\overline{\equiv}(x,y)\big) \to \overline{(Ez)}\,(Eu)\,[\Gamma(z)\,\&\,\Gamma(u)$$
$$\&\,\overline{\equiv}(z,u)\,\&\,\Lambda(x,u)\,\&\,\Lambda(x,z)\,\&\,\Lambda(y,z)\,\&\,\Lambda(y,u)\,]\,\}.$$

The conclusion may be written in corresponding fashion.

As a second example of a mathematical derivation, we take the proof of the *Theorem of the Transitivity of the Relation of Lesser to Greater*. This theorem, the expression of which by the formula

$$< (x,y)\,\&\, < (y,z) \to\, < (x,z)$$

is already known to us, we will formulate as relating to the theory of measurable quantities. We consider the argument places of the predicate $< (x, y)$ as referring to a definite kind of magnitude (e.g. lengths of line segments, or *positive* real numbers), and we consider the predicate as deriving from the addition of magnitudes. We introduce the symbol $\Phi(x, y, z)$ for the triadic predicate "x increased by y gives z" (or in arithmetic symbols: "$x + y = z$"). By means of this predicate, $< (x, y)$ may be defined by

$$(Eu)\,\Phi(x, u, y).$$

("There is a u which added to x gives y.")

If we substitute this definition in the statement of our theorem, the latter takes the following form:

$$[\,(Eu)\,\Phi(x, u, y)\,\&\,(Eu)\,\Phi(y, u, z)\,] \to (Eu)\,\Phi(x, u, z).$$

In this form the theorem may be proved, provided the following two postulates for the addition of magnitudes are assumed:

1. "Two magnitudes may always be added," *i.e.*

$$(Ez)\,\varPhi\,(x,\,y,\,z)\,.$$

2. "The addition of magnitudes obeys the assocative law

$$x + (y + z) = (x + y) + z,"$$

i.e.

$$[\varPhi\,(x,\,y,\,u)\,\&\,\varPhi\,(y,\,z,\,v)\,\&\,\varPhi\,(u,\,z,\,w)\,]\to\varPhi\,(x,\,v,\,w)\,.$$

The two postulates are in normal form, containing free variables. If we also put the theorem in normal form, we obtain:

$$(u)\,(v)\,(Ew)\,\big(\overline{\varPhi}(x,\,u,\,y)\,\mathrm{v}\,\overline{\varPhi}(y,\,v,\,z)\,\mathrm{v}\,\varPhi\,(x,\,w,\,z)\big)\,.$$

This may also be written:

$$(u)\,(v)\,(Ew)\,\big(\varPhi\,(x,\,u,\,y)\,\&\,\varPhi\,(y,\,v,\,z)\to\varPhi\,(x,\,w,\,z)\big)\,.$$

This formula may now be derived upon the basis of our postulates as follows:

By rewriting the variables, we obtain from the two postulates:

1. $(Ew)\,\varPhi\,(u,\,v,\,w)\,.$

2. $\big(\varPhi\,(x,\,u,\,y)\,\&\,\varPhi\,(u,\,v,\,w)\,\&\,\varPhi\,(y,\,v,\,z)\big)\to\varPhi\,(x,\,w,\,z)\,.$ If we apply Rule VII, p. 36, to the second postulate, it may be transformed into:

$$\varPhi\,(u,\,v,\,w)\to[\,\big(\varPhi\,(x,\,u,\,y)\,\&\,\varPhi\,(y,\,v,\,z)\big)\to\varPhi\,(x,\,w,\,z)\,]\,.$$

Using the rule belonging to Theorem 34, we may obtain therefrom:

$$(Ew)\,\varPhi\,(u,v,w)\to\ (Ew)\,[\,\big(\varPhi\,(x,u,y)\,\&\,\varPhi\,(y,v,z)\big)\to\varPhi\,(x,w,z)\,]\,.$$

Now since $(Ew)\,\varPhi\,(u,\,v,\,w)$ was assumed true, we obtain further

$$(Ew)\,\big(\varPhi\,(x,\,u,\,y)\,\&\,\varPhi\,(y,\,v,\,z)\to\varPhi\,(x,\,w,\,z)\big)\,.$$

From this the theorem follows when the universal quantifiers (u) and (v) are prefixed in accordance with Rule γ').

The method explained in this section of formal derivation from premises which are not universally valid logical formulas has its main application in the setting up of the primitive sentences or axioms for any particular field of knowledge and the derivation of the remaining theorems from them as consequences. It may even be said that only now is the concept of a system of axioms formulated with precision; for, a complete axiomatization should include not only the setting up of the axioms themselves, but also the exact statement of the logical means which enable us to derive new theorems from the axioms. We will examine, at the end of this section, the question of whether every statement which would intuitively be regarded as a consequence of the axioms can be obtained from them by means of the formal method of derivation.

Systems of axioms, insofar as they can be formalized at all within the framework of the restricted predicate calculus treated here, can be divided into two classes. By an *axiom system of the first order* we understand one in which the individual axioms contain no predicate variables but only predicate constants. (By axioms we understand here and in the following only those basic formulas which are characteristic of the field of knowledge under consideration, not the primitive logical formulas of §5, which form an invariable part of any system of axioms.) If predicate variables also occur in the axioms, then we speak of an *axiom system of the second order*. An exception to this classification is made only for the axioms of identity. These axioms have the following form, if we again employ the sign $\equiv$ for the predicate of identity:

$$\equiv (x, x),$$
$$\equiv (x, y) \rightarrow (F(x) \rightarrow F(y)).$$

(In the axiomatization of any particular field of knowledge, these axioms are usually omitted since they are of a purely logical nature. Cf. Chap. 4, § 1.) In the second of these axioms, there occurs a predicate variable. In spite of this, axiom systems in which predicate variables occur only in the axioms of identity, are counted among those of the first order. The reason is that the second axiom of identity, insofar as it is used within any given axiom system, can always be replaced by axioms without predicate variables. For, the place of this axiom may be taken by the axioms resulting from it by the substitution for F (in accordance with

Rule $a3$)) of the predicate constants occurring in the axiom system, and by the addition of axioms which express the symmetry and transitivity of identity. For example, if we have the predicate constants $\Phi(\ )$ and $\Psi(\ ,\ )$ in the axiom system, then the axioms of identity would be:

$$\equiv(x,\ x)$$
$$\equiv(x,\ y)\to\ \equiv(y,\ x)$$
$$(\equiv(x,\ y)\ \&\ \equiv(y,\ z)\,)\to\ \equiv(x,\ z)$$
$$\equiv(x,\ y)\to(\Phi(x)\to\Phi(y)\,)$$
$$\equiv(x,\ y)\to(\Psi(x,\ z)\to\Psi(y,\ z)\,)$$
$$\equiv(x,\ y)\to(\Psi(z,\ x)\to\Psi(z,\ y)\,)$$

and correspondingly in other cases. The rigorous proof of this replaceability is here omitted.

An example of an axiom system of second order is Peano's system of axioms for the natural numbers, since the formulation of the axiom of mathematical induction requires the use of a predicate variable. Another example is furnished by Zermelo's original formulation of an axiom system for the theory of sets, since the axiom of choice contains a predicate variable. An example of an axiom system of the first order is Hilbert's system of axioms for geometry, provided the axioms of continuity are excepted; another is the axiom system of group theory.

The following question now arises as a fundamental problem: *Is it possible to determine whether or not a given statement pertaining to a field of knowledge is a consequence of the axioms?*

We wish to show that this problem can be reduced to one of the pure predicate calculus, *i.e.* of the calculus set up in § 5, containing only predicate and individual variables. For the question of the logical dependence of a statement upon an axiom system can be reduced to the question of whether a given formula of the pure predicate calculus is or is not universally valid. However, this holds only if the axiom system is of the first order. We will illustrate the proof of this by a particular example.

In research on the logical interdependence of the various sets of axioms of geometry, there is a particularly interesting and important result which says: The special theorem of Pascal, which plays an essential role in the foundation of the theory of proportion without the use of axioms of continuity, cannot be proved if the axioms of incidence, order, and parallelism are the only ones used. It is a question of showing that the independence of Pascal's theorem with respect to the axioms mentioned is equivalent to the unprovability of a certain formula of the pure predicate calculus.

To begin with, we must express the axioms in question, as well as Pascal's special theorem, in terms of our calculus. Moreover, this must be done in such a way that we have to deal with only one class of objects. In order to avoid the use of more than one domain of individuals, we shall use here not the generally applicable method discussed earlier, but another which is specially adapted to our example. For this purpose we need only introduce, instead of the basic relation between points and straight lines ("the point x lies on the line y" or "the points x, y determine the line z"), a relation $Stl(x, y, z)$ among three points ("x, y, and z are collinear"). Likewise we shall take, instead of the basic relation between points and planes, a relation $Pl(x, y, z, u)$ among four points ("x, y, z, and u are coplanar").

To these two predicates we must add the relation of identity, $\equiv(x, y)$, as well as the relation of betweenness, $Bt(x, y, z)$ ("x lies between y and z").

By means of the four relations introduced, all of the axioms which occur in our problem, and Pascal's theorem as well, may be expressed by logical formulas. In this it is essential that the formulas be free of individual variables, which is accomplished by prefixing the universal quantifiers throughout. For example, the axiom "Through two points there passes only one straight line" is rendered by the formula:

$$(x)\,(y)\,(u)\,(v)\,\{[Stl(x, y, u)\ \&\ Stl(x, y, v)$$
$$\&\,\overline{\equiv}(x, y)\ \&\,\overline{\equiv}(u, v)]\to Stl(x, u, v)\},$$

in words: "If x, y, and u lie on a straight line, and if x, y, and v lie on a straight line, and if furthermore x is distinct from y and u is distinct from v, then x, u, and v also lie on a straight line." The axiom "If two planes have a point in common, then they have at least one other point in common," is rendered by the formula:

$$(x)\,(y)\,(z)\,(u)\,(v)\,(w)\,(p)\,\{[Pl(x, y, z, p)\;\&\;Pl(u, v, w, p)]$$
$$\to (Eq)\,(\overline{\equiv}(p, q)\;\&\;Pl(x, y, z, q)\;\&\;Pl(u, v, w, q))\}.$$

Corresponding to the axiom "If a straight line lying in the plane of a triangle intersects a side of this triangle, then it also intersects another side of the triangle," which is essential for ordering in the plane, we have the following formula:

$$(x)\,(y)\,(z)\,(u)\,(v)\,\{[Pl(x, y, z, u)\;\&\;\overline{Stl}(x, y, z)\;\&\;Bt(v, x, y)\;\&$$
$$\overline{Stl}(x, y, u)\;\&\;\overline{Stl}(z, u, v)]\to (Ew)\,[Stl(u, v, w)\;\&\;(Bt(w, x, z)$$
$$\mathrm{v}\,Bt(w, y, z))]\}.$$

It should be noted that in introducing the relations "*Stl*" and "*Pl*," their property of symmetry must be expressed in the form of axioms. Accordingly, we have to set up the formula:

$$(x)\,(y)\,(z)\,\{Stl(x, y, z)\to (Stl(x, z, y)\;\&\;Stl(y, x, z))\}$$

and the corresponding formula for *Pl*. Likewise, *the properties of the relation of identity* must be formulated as axioms:

$$(x)\,(y)\,\{\equiv(x, y)\to \equiv(y, x)\},$$
$$(x)\equiv(x, x),$$
$$(x)\,(y)\,(z)\,\{\equiv(x, z)\;\&\;\equiv(y, z)\to \equiv(x, y)\},$$
$$(x)\,(y)\,(z)\,(u)\,\{(\equiv(x, u)\;\&\;Stl(x, y, z))\to Stl(u, y, z)\},$$
$$(x)\,(y)\,(z)\,(u)\,(v)\,\{(\equiv(x, v)\;\&\;Pl(x, y, z, u))\to Pl(v, y, z, u)\},$$
$$(x)\,(y)\,(z)\,(u)\,\{(\equiv(x, y)\;\&\;Bt(x, u, z))\to Bt(y, u, z)\},$$
$$(x)\,(y)\,(u)\,(z)\,\{(\equiv(x, y)\;\&\;Bt(u, x, z))\to Bt(u, y, z)\}.$$

The last four formulas assert that in any of our relations identical objects may replace each other.

Let us now think of all the formulas for the axioms as being joined by &'s so as to form a single formula. This comprises the entire set of conditions imposed upon the predicates "$\equiv$," "*Stl*," "*Bt*," and "*Pl*" or, as one also says in an axiomatic theory, it contains the implicit definition of these predicates. As an abbreviation for this formula, we write:

$$\mathfrak{A}(\equiv, Stl, Bt, Pl).$$

Pascal's special theorem is expressed in ordinary terminology as follows: Let *ABC* be three points on a straight line, and *A'B'C'* be three points on a line which intersects the first, and let none of the six points coincide with the point of intersection of the two straight lines. If BC' is parallel to CB' and CA' is parallel to AC', then AB' is also parallel to BA'.

This theorem may also be expressed by a logical formula in which, of the above predicates, only "$\equiv$" and "Stl" occur. This formula will be designated by $\mathfrak{P}(\equiv, Stl)$.

The assertion we are considering now states that

$$\mathfrak{P}(\equiv, Stl)$$

cannot be proved from

$$\mathfrak{A}(\equiv, Stl, Bt, Pl)$$

The actual geometric meanings of $\equiv$, Stl, Bt, and Pl no longer play a role in this assertion. For, in accordance with the axiomatic standpoint, any proof of a theorem from the geometric axioms may not use anything of the basic relations introduced except what is explicitly formulated in the axioms.

Therefore, we can eliminate these predicates entirely and replace them by four predicate variables, of course with the same number of arguments:

$$F(x, y) ; \quad G(x, y, z) ; \quad H(x, y, z) ; \quad K(x, y, z, u).$$

The provability of Pascal's theorem would mean that for any four such predicates F, G, H, and K, satisfying

$$\mathfrak{A}(F, G, H, K),$$

$\mathfrak{P}(F, G)$ also holds, *i.e.* that

$$\mathfrak{A}(F, G, H, K) \to \mathfrak{P}(F, G)$$

is a universally valid formula. We have thus to show that this is not the case.

Similarly we can find a formula of the predicate calculus corresponding to any geometric theorem in such a way that the theorem is a consequence of the axioms if and only if the logical formula is universally valid. Similarly, questions of *consistency* can be reduced to the question of the universal validity of certain formulas. For example, the question of whether the geometric axioms combined in the formula

$$\mathfrak{A}(\equiv, Stl, Bt, Pl)$$

are logically compatible is equivalent to the question of whether

$$\overline{\mathfrak{A}}(F, G, H, K)$$

fails to be a universally valid formula.

We can further say that any consequence of an axiom system of the first order can also be derived from it by means of the formal method of derivation set forth at the beginning of this section. For, the universally valid formula expressing the logical dependence of the theorem upon the axioms is also provable, according to § 10. The Rule of Implication will yield the theorem itself after substitution of the predicate constants for the predicate variables in this formula.

As has already been mentioned, our last remarks concerning the equivalence of the dependence of a theorem upon an axiom system to the universal validity of a formula of the predicate calculus apply only to axiom systems of the first order. However, for the axiom systems of the second order a similar situation holds. Only, the valid formula in question is no longer expressible in the restricted predicate calculus, but belongs to the extended predicate calculus, to be treated in Chapter 4.

§ 12. The Decision Problem

From the considerations of the preceding section, there emerges the fundamental importance of determining whether or not a given formula of the predicate calculus is universally valid. According to the definition given in § 5, the universal validity of a formula means the same as its universal validity in every domain of individuals. The problem just mentioned is called the *problem of the universal validity* of a formula. More precisely, instead of universal validity one should speak of universal validity in every domain of individuals. The universally valid formulas of the predicate calculus are, by § 10, precisely those formulas which are deducible from the axiom system of § 5. This fact does not yield a solution of the problem of universal validity, since we have no general criterion for the deducibility of a formula.

A formula of the pure predicate calculus, *i.e.* one containing no constants, is called *satisfiable* in a domain of individuals if the sentential variables can be replaced by the values truth and falsehood, the predicate variables by predicate constants defined in the domain, and the free individual variables by individual constants, in such a way that the formula goes over into a true sentence. If we simply call a formula satisfiable, then we mean that there exists a domain of individuals in which it is satisfiable. If a formula $\mathfrak{A}$ is not universally valid in any given domain of individuals, then clearly $\overline{\mathfrak{A}}$ is satisfiable in that domain, and conversely. Similarly, the universal validity in general of a formula $\overline{\mathfrak{A}}$ and the satisfiability of $\mathfrak{A}$ are contradictory opposites of each other.

It is customary to refer to the two equivalent problems of *universal validity* and *satisfiability* by the common name of the *decision problem* of the restricted predicate calculus. As noted in § 11, we are justified in calling it the main problem of mathematical logic.

We shall illustrate the concepts of universal validity and satisfiability by some examples. Among the universally valid formulas are, for example, all those which are deducible from the logical axioms, for instance Theorems 21 through 36 of § 6. All universally valid formulas are of course also satisfiable. The formula

$$(Ex)F(x),$$

while of course not universally valid, is satisfiable; we need only take for F the predicate "to be identical with itself," in any given domain of individuals. This applies not only to one but even to all individuals. From this, it follows that

$$(x)F(x)$$

is also satisfiable. Further,

$$(x)\overline{F}(x, x) \mathbin{\&} (x)(Ey)F(x, y)$$

is satisfiable. One need only take the whole numbers as the domain of individuals, and substitute the predicate $x < y$ for $F(x, y)$. An example of a non-satisfiable formula is

$$(Ex)\,(y)\,\big(F(x, x)\;\&\;\overline{F}(x, y)\big),$$

since its negation

$$(x)\,(Ey)\,\big(\overline{F}(x, x)\;\text{v}\;F(x, y)\big)$$

is a valid formula. In fact, for each x there is a y of the kind required, since we can take y to be equl to x itself.

There is also a *stricter form* of the decision problem. A formula which is satisfiable in some domain of individuals need not be satisfiable in every domain of individuals. For example, the formula

$$(Ex)\,(Ey)\,\big(F(x)\;\&\;\overline{F}(y)\big)$$

is certainly satisfiable. One need only take as the domain of individuals the domain consisting of 0 and 1, and substitute for F the predicate "$x = 0$." There are then an x and a y such that $x = 0$ and $y \neq 0$, namely, 0 and 1. This formula, however, is not satisfiable in a domain of individuals consisting of only a single element, since a predicate cannot simultaneously hold and not hold for the same thing. Likewise the negation

$$(x)\,(y)\,\big(\overline{F}(x)\;\text{v}\;F(y)\big)$$

of the above formula is universally valid in any domain containing only one individual, but not otherwise.

If satisfiability or universal validity holds for a formula in a given domain of individuals, then it holds also in every other domain of individuals with the same cardinal number, as can readily be seen by a one-to-one mapping of the domains upon each other. Therefore, disregarding those formulas which are universally valid (or satisfiable) in every domain of individuals, and disregarding those which have this property in no domain, *the assertion of the universal validity (or satisfiability) of a logical formula is equivalent to a statement about the number of individuals.* In the broadest sense, the decision problem can be considered solved if we have a method which permits us to decide for any given formula *in which domains of individuals it is universally valid (or satisfiable) and in which it is not.*

As regards the relation to one another of the two forms of the decision problem, we already had a remarkable theorem in § 10.

If a formula is universally valid in a denumerably infinite domain, then it is universally valid in any domain, that is, it is a universally valid formula.

The formulation of this theorem in terms of satisfiability would be:

If a formula is satisfiable at all, then the satisfiability obtains also in a denumerably infinite domain of individuals.

Further, as an extension (much more trivial, to be sure) of this theorem, we have:

If a formula is satisfiable in any domain of individuals whatsoever, then it is also satisfiable in any domain containing a larger number of individuals.

In fact, one can easily extend the definition of the predicates which satisfy a formula in a domain (J) in such a way that they are satisfied also in a domain (J') which contains (J) as a subdomain. For this purpose we select any element a from (J) and extend the definition of the predicates to the domain (J') by proceeding as though all elements of (J') not belonging to (J) were identical with a. For example, if we have for the domain (J) a "satisfying" predicate Φ with n argument places, then the corresponding predicate Ψ in (J') is defined as follows: For all $x_1, x_2, \ldots, x_n$ of (J'),

$$\Psi(x_1, x_2, \ldots, x_n) \sim \Phi(\mathfrak{x}_1, \mathfrak{x}_2, \ldots, \mathfrak{x}_n)$$

holds. Here $\mathfrak{x}_i$ is identical with x_i if x_i belongs to (J), otherwise it is the same as a. From the way in which the predicates are defined there then follows satisfiability in the domain (J'). This will not be set forth here in detail.

In case the domain of individuals contains a definite finite number of members, the decision concerning universal validity, or concerning satisfiability, can always be made.

In fact, in this case the universal quantifiers can be replaced by a finite conjunction, the existential quantifiers by a finite disjunction, of sentences; and the universal validity, or satisfiability, of the formula in the finite domain is reduced to the universal validity or satisfiability, respectively, of a formula of the sentential calculus.

An example will make this clearer. Let the problem be to examine the satisfiability of the formula

$$(Ex)\,(y)\,\big(F(x,x)\,\&\,\overline{F}(x,y)\big)$$

in a domain consisting of two individuals. If we let the members of this domain be 0 and 1, then for this domain every formula $(Ex)\,\mathfrak{A}(x)$ is equivalent to $\mathfrak{A}(0)\,\text{v}\,\mathfrak{A}(1)$, and every formula $(x)\,\mathfrak{A}(x)$ to $\mathfrak{A}(0)\,\&\,\mathfrak{A}(1)$. Hence the above formula can first be replaced by

$$(y)\,\big(F(0,0)\,\&\,\overline{F}(0,y)\big)\,\text{v}\,(y)\,\big(F(1,1)\,\&\,\overline{F}(1,y)\big),$$

and further by

$$\big(F(0,0)\,\&\,\overline{F}(0,0)\,\&\,F(0,0)\,\&\,\overline{F}(0,1)\big)$$
$$\text{v}\,\big(F(1,1)\,\&\,\overline{F}(1,0)\,\&\,F(1,1)\,\&\,\overline{F}(1,1)\big).$$

It is now a matter of replacing the $F(0,0)$, $F(0,1)$, etc. by true and false sentences in such a way that the formula will have the value truth. In other words, the satisfiability of the formula in a domain of two individuals is reduced to the satisfiability of the sentential formula

$$(A\,\&\,\overline{A}\,\&\,A\,\&\,\overline{B})\,\text{v}\,(C\,\&\,\overline{D}\,\&\,C\,\&\,\overline{C}).$$

From the last theorems there follows: *If it can be shown for a given formula that it is satisfiable if and only if it is satisfiable in a domain of individuals with a definite finite number k of individuals, then the problem of its satisfiability is decided for all domains of individuals.*

For, first of all, we can determine whether the formula is satisfiable in a domain of k individuals. If this is not the case, then the formula is satisfiable in no domain. But if it can be satisfied in this domain, then it can also be satisfied in all domains with a larger number of individuals. It then remains only to investigate its satisfiability in domains with $1, 2, \ldots, k-1$ individuals, which can always be done.

At the same time it should be noted that one does not achieve in this way a general solution of the decision problem. *For there are formulas which are satisfiable in no finite domain of individuals, but which are satisfiable in a domain with infinitely many individuals.* One of these formulas, for example, is

$$(x)\,(Ey)\,F(x, y) \;\&\; (x)\,\overline{F}(x, x) \;\&\; (x)\,(y)\,(z)\,[\,(F(x, y) \;\&\; \\ F(y, z)\,) \to F(x, z)\,].$$

This formula is satisfied, for example, in the domain of natural numbers, by the predicate $x < y$. On the other hand, to assume its satisfiability in a domain with a finite number of individuals immediately yields a contradiction. Let Φ, say, be the predicate which satisfies it. Because of the truth of $(x)\,(Ey)\,\Phi(x, y)$, there would exist a chain of elements $a_1, a_2, a_3, \ldots$ capable of indefinite extension and such that $\Phi(a_i, a_{i+1})$ always holds. Because of the assumed finiteness of the domain of individuals, there would be an i and a k $(k > i)$ such that a_i and a_k are the same element. From

$$(x)\,(y)\,(z)\,\{\,[\Phi(x, y) \;\&\; \Phi(y, z)\,] \to \Phi(x, z)\}$$

there would then follow $\Phi(a_i, a_i)$, whereas in fact $(x)\,\overline{\Phi}(x, x)$ is the case.

While the decision problem was easy to solve in the sentential calculus, e.g. by using the conjunctive or disjunctive normal form (cf. Chap. I, §§ 4 and 6, and also § 8), in the predicate calculus it presents a very difficult problem which as a whole remains unsolved. Certain reasons, given in more detail below, even make the search for a complete solution appear hopeless. Because of the central position of the problem, however, even the attempts to give a decision procedure at least for as large a class of formulas as possible are of great interest. In what follows, we give the chief results in this direction.

In all the arguments that follow we shall suppose that we have to deal with formulas no longer containing free individual variables. Before turning to the special cases in which the decision problem has been solved, we will discuss a few general theorems related to that problem. Some of these theorems have already been discussed in § 8, namely those concerning the *prenex* and *Skolem normal form*. They have the advantage of allowing us without loss of generality to consider only formulas of a special normal or reduced form in our arguments relating to validity or satisfiability. For this reason they are also called *reduction theorems*. For instance, Skolem's theorem (formulated here with respect to satisfiability) states that for any given formula of the predicate calculus we can find another formula with a prefix of the form

$$(x_1) \ldots (x_m) (Ey_1) \ldots (Ey_n),$$

whose satisfiability is equivalent to the satisfiability of the given formula. Thus we need consider only formulas which have a prefix of the above kind, when dealing with the problem of satisfiability.

Further theorems of this kind also concern either the reduction of the formulas to those with certain prefixes, or a reduction of the number of arguments in the predicate variables occurring, or a reduction of the number of predicate variables, etc. Of the numerous results in this direction, we mention only the following:

For any formula, we may find another which is equivalent to the first as to satisfiability, and which contains only monadic and dyadic predicate variables.[1] Further, we may even restrict ourselves to such formulas as contain only a single dyadic predicate variable and whose prefix is of the form[2]

$$(Ex_1) \ldots (Ex_m) (y_1) (y_2) (Ez) (u_1) \ldots (u_n).$$

Further, we may restrict ourselves in the problem of satisfiability to formulas having a prefix of the form[3]

$$(x_1) (x_2) (x_3) (Ey_1) \ldots (Ey_n).$$

---

[1] L. Löwenheim, *loc. cit.* (see § 10).

[2] L. Kalmár, *Zurückführung des Entscheidungsproblems auf den Fall von Formeln mit einer einzigen binären Funktionsvariablen.* Comp. Math. Vol. 4 (1936). Cf. also the earlier papers of that author listed therein.

[3] K. Gödel, *Zum Entscheidungsproblem des logischen Funktionenkalküls.* Mh. Math. Physik, Vol. 40 (1933).

Finally, it is sufficient, in the case of the problem of satisfiability, to consider such formulas as have a prefix of the form[1]

$$(Ex)\,(y)\,(Ez)\,(u_1)\ldots(u_n).$$

For proofs of these theorems, the reader is referred to the original papers cited.[2]

We now report on the most important special cases in which a successful solution of the decision problem has been reached. These special cases constitute a certain parallel to the above reduction theorems. The theorem that for any formula of the predicate calculus we can find one which is equivalent in respect to satisfiability and which contains only monadic and dyadic predicate variables, has its analogy in the theorem that *the decision problem has been solved for all formulas containing only monadic predicate variables.* Similarly, the possibility of reducing the decision problem to the case of formulas with certain definite prefixes corresponds to the fact that for certain classes of prefixes a solution of the decision problem has been attained.

The possibility, as a matter of principle, of decision in the case of monadic predicates was first recognized by L. Löwenheim.[3] Simpler proofs have been given[4] by T. Skolem[5] and H. Behmann.[6] These methods of proof extend beyond the restricted predicate calculus, since they solve the decision problem in the case of monadic predicates also for the predicate calculus of the second

---

[1] W. Ackermann, *Beiträge zum Entscheidungsproblem der mathematischen Logik.* Math. Ann. Vol. 112 (1936).

[2] Further reduction theorems are found in: J. Pepis, *Beiträge zur Reduktionstheorie des logischen Entscheidungsproblems.* Acta. Lit. Szeged Vol. 8 (1936). T. Skolem, *Einige Reduktionen des Entscheidungsproblems.* Avh. Vid. Akad. Oslo, I Mat.-nat. Klasse 1936, No. 6.

[3] L. Löwenheim, *loc. cit.*

[4] An especially lucid treatment of the monadic predicate calculus is found in Hilbert-Bernays, *Grundlagen der Mathematik* I (cf. esp. § 5, pp. 194, 195).

[5] T. Skolem, *Untersuchungen über die Axiome des Klassenkalküls und über Produktation- und Summationsprobleme, welche gewisse Klassen von Aussagen betreffen.* Vid. Skrifter I, Mat.-nat. Klasse 1919, No. 3.

[6] H. Behmann, *Beiträge zur Algebra der Logik und zum Entscheidungsproblem.* Math. Ann. Vol. 86 (1922).

order, to be treated in Chapter IV. We shall return to this point in the next chapter.

In the following discussion it is, incidentally, more convenient to consider the problem of universal validity. We can demonstrate the decision procedure for formulas of the restricted predicate calculus which contain only monadic predicate variables, as follows.

Let such a formula be given. Let k be the number of different predicate symbols $A, B, \ldots, K$ occurring in this formula. We now assert: If the formula is universally valid in any domain of not more than 2^k individuals, then it is universally valid in any domain.

For proof we assume that the formula under consideration yields a false sentence for a certain system of more than 2^k individuals upon replacement of the predicate variables $A, B, \ldots, K$ by the predicate constants $A_0, B_0, \ldots, K_0$. From this sentence we will then derive another false sentence which likewise is obtained by a specialization of the given formula and which refers to a domain of at most 2^k individuals.

We divide the individuals which figure in the above false sentence (with the predicates $A_0, B_0, \ldots, K_0$) into classes by putting two objects a and b into the same class if the sentences

$$A_0(a), B_0(a), \ldots, K_0(a)$$

are respectively of the same truth values as

$$A_0(b), B_0(b), \ldots, K_0(b),$$

that is,

$A_0(a)$ has the same truth value as $A_0(b)$,
$B_0(a)$ has the same truth value as $B_0(b)$,
. . . .
$K_0(a)$ has the same truth value as $K_0(b)$.

In this way we obtain at most 2^k classes. For, $A_0(a)$ must be either true or false for the individual a; similarly with $B_0(a)$, etc. Altogether there are thus only 2^k possibilities for the distribution of truth and falsehood among the sentences

$$A_0(a), B_0(a), \ldots, K_0(a),$$

and if for two individuals we have the same distribution, they belong to the same class.

Let $a_1, a_2, \ldots, a_n$ be the different classes thus obtained, so that $n \leq 2^k$. We now take the set of classes $a_1, a_2, \ldots, a_n$ as a new domain of individuals. With respect to these individuals we define k predicates $A_1, B_1, \ldots, K_1$ as follows: A_1 is to hold for the class a_p $(p = 1, \ldots, n)$ if and only if A_0 holds for the original individuals belonging to a_p. The definitions of $B_1, \ldots, K_1$ are analogous.

Now consider any arbitrary sentence constructed from the predicates $A_0, B_0, \ldots, K_0$ by means of the logical symbols and replace A_0 by A_1, B_0 by $B_1, \ldots, K_0$ by K_1, and take the classes $a_1, a_2, \ldots, a_n$, as the values of the individual variables, and replace each of the individual constants which may occur in the sentences by the class to which it belongs. Then the sentence goes over into one with the same truth value.

The truth of this assertion is immediately apparent in case the sentence in question has no quantifiers. We prove it in the general case by writing the sentence in normal form and carrying out mathematical induction on the number of prefixed quantifiers.

From this theorem it now follows in particular that the false sentence which by assumption is obtained from the given formula by replacing the predicate variables $A, B, \ldots, K$ with the predicates $A_0, B_0, \ldots, K_0$, is transformed into another false sentence if we replace the predicates $A_0, B_0, \ldots, K_0$ by $A_1, B_1, \ldots, K_1$ and take the classes $a_1, a_2, \ldots, a_n$ as the values of the individual variables.

Accordingly, we need to carry out the decision only for the case of at most 2^k, hence a finite number, of objects. For this case, however, the decision may be accomplished by a finite process, as we have seen.

If we now consider once more those formulas in which arbitrary predicate variables occur, then a decision procedure can easily be given for the universal validity of those formulas in which *the prefix consists solely of universal quantifiers, or solely of existential quantifiers, or in which all the universal quantifiers precede all the existential quantifiers.*

To begin with, let us consider a formula of the first type, *i.e.* a formula of the form

$$(x_1)(x_2) \ldots (x_m) \, \mathfrak{A}(x_1, x_2, \ldots, x_m)$$

in which the $\mathfrak{A}(x_1, x_2, \ldots, x_m)$ contains no additional quantifiers. *This formula is universally valid if and only if it is universally valid in a domain of m individuals.*

In fact, if the formula were not universally valid for a domain with a larger number than m of individuals, then there would exist in this domain elements $a_1, a_2, \ldots, a_m$, and predicate constants, for which

$$\mathfrak{A}(a_1, a_2, \ldots, a_m)$$

is a false formula. However it is apparent that in this case we would not have universal validity in the domain $(a_1, a_2, \ldots, a_m)$.

Next, a formula

$$(Ex_1) \ldots (Ex_m) \mathfrak{A}(x_1, \ldots, x_m),$$

in which the prefix consists solely of existential quantifiers, is universally valid if it has universal validity in a domain with only one individual.

In fact, if the above formula is not universally valid, then neither is the formula

$$(Ex) \mathfrak{A}(x, x, \ldots, x),$$

which represents a stronger assertion. Thus there exists a domain with an element a and predicate constants, such that $\mathfrak{A}(a, \ldots, a)$ can be made into a false formula. We would then not have universal validity in the domain consisting of the single element a.

In the same simple way, it can also be shown that the formulas

$$(x_1) \ldots (x_m)(Ey_1) \ldots (Ey_n) \mathfrak{A}(x_1, \ldots, x_m, y_1, \ldots, y_n),$$

in which all the universal quantifiers precede all the existential quantifiers, are universally valid provided that universal validity obtains in a domain with m individuals. In fact, we may form the disjunction of all possible formulas

$$\mathfrak{A}(x_1, \ldots, x_m, x_{i_1}, \ldots, x_{i_n})$$

which arise from $\mathfrak{A}(x_1, \ldots, x_m, y_1, \ldots, y_n)$ by replacing $y_1, \ldots, y_n$ in any way by variables from the set $x_1, \ldots, x_m$. We shall designate this disjunction by $\mathfrak{B}(x_1, \ldots, x_m)$. Clearly, from the universal validity for a domain of m individuals of

$$(x_1) \ldots (x_m) (Ey_1) \ldots (Ey_n) \mathfrak{A}(x_1, \ldots, x_m, y_1, \ldots, y_n),$$

there follows that of $(x_1) \ldots (x_m) \mathfrak{B}(x_1, \ldots, x_m)$ and therefore also the universal validity for any domain of

$$(x_1) \ldots (x_m) \mathfrak{B}(x_1, \ldots, x_m).$$

However, since

$$(x_1) \ldots (x_m) \mathfrak{B}(x_1, \ldots, x_m)$$

represents a stronger statement than

$$(x_1) \ldots (x_m) (Ey_1) \ldots (Ey_n) \mathfrak{A}(x_1, \ldots, x_m, y_1, \ldots, y_n),$$

our assertion is proved.[1]

Of the other special cases of the decision problem which have been solved, in which, incidentally, success is not attained by such simple means, we shall discuss only the following. For such formulas as have a prefix of the form

$$(x_1) \ldots (x_m) (Ey_1) (Ey_2) (z_1) \ldots (z_n),$$

a decision procedure for universal validity may be given.[2] In this case also, a decision concerning universal validity in general can be based upon a decision concerning universal validity in a definite finite domain of individuals. With these results, we have exhausted the types of prefixes for which we can achieve a deci-

---

[1] The last-mentioned special cases of the decision problem were solved in the paper of P. Bernays and M. Schönfinkel, *Zum Entscheidungsproblem der mathematischen Logik*, Math. Ann. Vol. 99 (1928).

[2] Cf. K. Gödel, *loc. cit.* (Preliminary presentation earlier in Erg. Wien Math. Koll. Vol. 2 (1932)).—L. Kalmár, *Über die Erfüllbarkeit derjenigen Zählausdrücke, welche in der Normalform zwei benachbarte Allzeichen enthalten.* Math. Ann. Vol. 108 (1932).—K. Schütte, *Untersuchungen zum Entscheidungsproblem der mathematischen Logik.* Math. Ann. Vol. 109 (1934).—*Über die Erfüllbarkeit einer Klasse von logischen Formeln.* Math. Ann. Vol. 110 (1934).—For the case in which the above prefix contains only one existential quantifier, instead of two, the solution had been obtained earlier by W. Ackermann and T. Skolem. Cf. W. Ackermann, *Über die Erfüllbarkeit gewisser Zählausdrücke.* Math. Ann. Vol. 100 (1928).—T. Skolem, *Über die mathematische Logik.* Norsk. Mat. Tidskr. Vol. 10 (1928). A special case of the last kind was already treated in the paper cited in footnote 1 above.

sion concerning universal validity by the above methods. For all other prefixes we can actually find formulas which are universally valid in any finite domain of individuals, but not in infinite domains.[1]

Results by A. Church based on papers by K. Gödel show that the quest for a general solution of the decision problem must be regarded as hopeless.[2] We cannot report on these researches in detail within the limits of this book. We shall only remark that a general method of decision would consist of a certain recursive procedure for the individual formulas which would finally yield for each formula the value truth or the value falsehood. Church's work proves, however, the non-existence of such a recursive procedure; at least, the necessary recursions would not fall under the general type of recursion set up by Church, who has given to the somewhat vague intuitive concept of recursion a certain precise formalization.

To avoid misunderstanding, it should be noted that the impossibility of a general decision procedure does not mean that we can find definite formulas whose universal validity has been proved not to be decidable. To assume the existence of such a proof would in fact lead to an immediate contradiction. From such a proof it would follow that the formula would not be deducible from the axiom system of § 5. But by the completeness theorem of § 10, the satisfiability of the contradictory of the formula could then be proved. Thus the universal validity would be decided after all, viz. in the negative. In any case, therefore, the task of extending the class of formulas for which the decision is solved, remains rewarding and significant.

---

[1] Cf. the first paper by K. Schütte cited in footnote 2, p. 123.

[2] A. Church, *An unsolvable problem of elementary number theory.* Am. J. of Math. Vol. 58 (1936),—*A note on the Entscheidungsproblem; Correction to a note on the Entscheidungsproblem,* J. Symb. Logic. Vol. 1 (1936).

CHAPTER IV

THE EXTENDED PREDICATE CALCULUS

§ 1. The Predicate Calculus of Second Order

We can effect the first extension of the restricted predicate calculus, or, as it is also called, the predicate calculus of first order, by taking into account the fact that the formalism of this calculus is clearly not a closed system. Thus, while we can express that a formula stands for a true sentence for all values of the predicate variables which occur in it, we are unable to express the opposite of this assertion. For if we put a negation bar over the entire formula, then it means that the formula is to be a false sentence for all values of the predicate variables. There is, however, the possibility that a formula stands for an assertion which is neither true for all values of the predicate variables nor false for all values of the predicate variables. For example, the formula $(x)F(x)$ is certainly not universally valid for any domain of individuals, but neither is the formula $\overline{(x)F(x)}$. In order to express the fact that $(x)F(x)$ is not universally valid, we must have an existential quantifier for predicates.

Thus we are led to a natural extension of the predicate calculus of first order *by applying universal and existential quantifiers also to sentential and predicate variables, and by distinguishing between free and bound variables of that kind.*

The concept of logical formula, as defined in § 4, then undergoes a corresponding extension. We arrive at a *predicate calculus of second order.*

Some examples will serve to illustrate the increased possibility of expression. The formula

$$(P)\,(x)\,(P(x) \vee \overline{P}(x))$$

125

says that

$$(x)\,(P(x) \vee \overline{P}(x))$$

holds for every predicate P. The formula

$$(A)\,(F)\,\{\,(x)\,[A \to F(x)] \sim [A \to (x)F(x)]\,\}$$

expresses the fact that the relation between sentences and predicates defined by

$$(x)\,(A \to F(x)) \sim (A \to (x)F(x))$$

holds for any sentences and predicates whatever.

A case of the same sort is found in the *symbolic formulation of the principle of mathematical induction*. The content of this principle can be expressed as follows:

"If a predicate holds for the number 1, and if when it holds for any particular number, it holds also for its successor, then the predicate holds for every number."

If we introduce the sign $Seq\,(x,\,y)$ to denote the relation of a number to its successor, then we can express the principle by postulating

$$\{P(1)\,\&\,(x)\,(y)\,[P(x)\,\&\,Seq\,(x,\,y) \to P(y)]\} \to (x)P(x)$$

as a universally valid formula for the domain of natural numbers.

If we further wish to express explicitly in the symbolism that the formula is to hold for all predicates P, we can do this by prefixing the universal quantifier (P).

The *definition of identity* constitutes a further characteristic case. The relation of identity may be defined in terms of the basic logical relations by calling x identical with y if any predicate which holds for x also holds for y and vice versa. In the sense of this definition the sign $\equiv(x,\,y)$ for identity may be regarded as an abbreviation for the expression

$$(F)\,(F(x) \sim F(y)).$$

In the above cases the use of the universal quantifier, although convenient, is not really essential. However, there are cases in which the use of the universal quantifier is necessary, if important modes of expression are not to be sacrificed.

If, for example, we wish to state that every predicate $R(x, y)$ equivalent to the predicate of identity also has the property of symmetry, we must write this as follows:

$$(R)\{(x)(y)[R(x, y) \sim (F)(F(x) \sim F(y))]$$
$$\rightarrow (x)(y)(R(x, y) \rightarrow R(y, x))\}.$$

Here the universal quantifier (F) cannot be left out without altering the meaning of the expression.

In the same way, as already mentioned above, the universal quantifier is essential if we wish to deny that a given expression is a true formula for all of the values of the predicate variables occurring in it. In order to assert, say, that $(x)(y)F(x, y)$ is not a universally valid formula, we can use the formula

$$\overline{(F)}(x)(y)F(x, y)$$

or the equivalent formula

$$(EF)(Ex)(Ey)\overline{F}(x, y).$$

The same holds for many theorems of logic which are general statements about sentences and predicates. It holds, for instance, for the theorem that there is for every sentence X a sentence Y such that, of the two sentences, one and only one is true (*i.e.,* the theorem of the existence of the contradictory of a sentence). In the extended symbolism this may be rendered thus:

$$(X)(EY)(X \vee Y \& \overline{X \& Y}).$$

This theorem, on the other hand, could not have been rendered in the restricted symbolism.

The extension of the symbolism enables us to formulate symbolically problems and their solutions for which we formerly had to use a roundabout intuitive description. For instance, let us recall the arguments used in § 8 of the first chapter. The results obtained there may be rendered by the following formulas:

$$(X)(A_1X \& A_2\overline{X}) \sim A_1 \& A_2,$$
$$(EX)(A_1X \& A_2\overline{X}) \sim A_1 \vee A_2.$$

These formulas give *a rule by which an expression containing quantifiers for sentential variables may be replaced by an equi-*

valent expression in which these quantifiers no longer occur. We simply develop the expression in successive steps, beginning with the variable which belongs to the innermost quantifier, and remove this variable in accordance with the elimination rule expressed in the formulas. For example, from

$$(X_1) (X_2) (A_1 X_1 X_2 \mathbin{\&} A_2 X_1 \overline{X}_2 \mathbin{\&} A_3 \overline{X}_1 X_2 \mathbin{\&} A_4 \overline{X}_1 \overline{X}_2),$$

there is obtained

$$(X_1) ((A_1 \mathbin{\&} A_2) X_1 \mathbin{\&} (A_3 \mathbin{\&} A_4) \overline{X}_1)$$

by the removal of the quantifier (X_2), and further

$$A_1 \mathbin{\&} A_2 \mathbin{\&} A_3 \mathbin{\&} A_4.$$

This *elimination rule*, which we are now able to formulate symbolically, enables us to recognize the truth or the falsehood of formulas in which only sentential variables and quantifiers belonging to them occur. For example, in the formula

$$(X) (EY) (XY \mathbin{\&} \overline{X} \mathbin{\&} Y),$$

mentioned above, we first develop $XY \mathbin{\&} \overline{X} \mathbin{\&} Y$ with respect to Y, and obtain

$$(X) (EY) (XY \mathbin{\&} \overline{X}\overline{Y}).$$

The elimination of the innermost quantifier yields

$$(X) (X\overline{X}).$$

$X\overline{X}$, however, is a universally valid expression, and therefore $(X) (EY) (XY \mathbin{\&} \overline{X} \mathbin{\&} Y)$ is a valid formula.

Both forms of the decision problem for the restricted predicate calculus may now be formulated symbolically. To the universal validity and to the satisfiability of, say, the formula

$$(Ex) (y) (F(x, x) \mathbin{v} \overline{F}(y, y) \mathbin{v} G(x, y))$$

in some given domain of individuals, there corresponds in the extended calculus the validity in this domain of the formulas

$$(F) (G) (Ex) (y) (F(x, x) \mathbin{v} \overline{F}(y, y) \mathbin{v} G(x, y))$$

and

$$(EF) (EG) (Ex) (y) (F(x, x) \mathbin{v} \overline{F}(y, y) \mathbin{v} G(x, y)),$$

respectively.

In the interpretation of logical formulas it is always sufficient to consider those formulas which contain no free variables of any sort, since we may eliminate free variables by prefixing the corresponding universal quantifiers to a formula in which they occur. Consequently, in the calculus of second order there can be no question of universal validity or of satisfiability in the former sense. In spite of this, the meaning of the formulas is not yet uniquely determined by the symbolism alone as long as we do not know the choice of the domain of individuals. For example,

$$(EF)\,(Ex)\,(Ey)\,(F(x)\,\&\,\overline{F}(y))$$

stands for a false sentence if the domain of individuals consists of only one element, but otherwise it always stands for a true sentence.

By the *universally valid* formulas of the calculus we shall now understand those formulas which are true for arbitrary choice of the domain of individuals. Note that universal validity in this sense refers only to arbitrary choice of domain of individuals and not to arbitrary choice of sentences or predicates. Correspondingly, one can call a formula satisfiable if there exists a domain of individuals for which the formula is a true sentence. Once more, universal validity of a formula is equivalent to the non-satisfiability of the negation of the formula.

Among the universally valid formulas are all the universally valid formulas of the restricted predicate calculus, and others as well. If, as before, $\equiv(x, y)$ is used as an abbreviation for $(F)\,(F(x) \sim F(y))$, *i.e.*, for the predicate of identity, then

$$(x)\equiv(x, x) \quad \text{and} \quad (x)\,(y)\,(\equiv(x, y) \to \,\equiv(y, x))$$

are universally valid formulas. Further examples are

$$(EF)\,(Ex)F(x)$$

and

$$(F)\,(EG)\,(x)\,(y)\,(F(x, y)\,\vee\,\overline{G}(x, y)).$$

Among the satisfiable formulas there are all those that are obtained from satisfiable formulas of the restricted predicate calculus by prefixing the relevant existential quantifier for predicates, and there are others as well. For example,

$$(F)\,((Ex)F(x) \to (x)F(x))$$

is also a satisfiable formula.

The next question would seem to be whether (as in the predicate calculus of first order) a system of primitive logical formulas can be given here from which all the remaining universally valid formulas can be deduced by proceeding according to certain rules. Let us remark at once that *a complete axiom system for the universally valid formulas of the predicate calculus of second order does not exist.* Rather, as K. Gödel has shown, for any system of primitive formulas and rules of inference we can find universally valid formulas which cannot be deduced.[1] Nevertheless the following system should suffice for most purposes:

First, we take all the primitive formulas and rules of inference of the restricted predicate calculus but think of the rules of inference now as applying to the extended concept of formula. To the primitive formula e) we may add arbitrarily many primitive formulas of the form

$$(F)\,\mathfrak{A}(F) \to \mathfrak{A}(G).$$

Here $\mathfrak{A}(F)$ is a formula which contains the free predicate variable F, but not G, and $\mathfrak{A}(G)$ is the formula which is obtained from $\mathfrak{A}(F)$ by substituting G for F in $\mathfrak{A}(F)$ in accordance with Rule $a3$). Likewise we may add as primitive formulas any number of formulas of the form

$$\mathfrak{A}(G) \to (EF)\,\mathfrak{A}(F).$$

In addition, we have primitive formulas which are closely related to the axiom of choice of set theory. The first of these formulas is

g) $(EF)\{(x)\,[(Ey)\,G(x,y) \to (Ey)\,(F(x,y)\ \&\ G(x,y))]$
    $\&\ (x)\,(y)\,(z)\,[F(x,y)\ \&\ F(x,z) \to\ \equiv(y,z)]\}.$

The meaning of this formula is the following: A predicate $G(x,y)$ associates certain values of y with those x for which

---

[1] K. Gödel, *Über formal unentscheidbare Sätze der Principia Mathematica und verwandter Systeme.* Mh. Math. Physik Vol. 38 (1931).

there exists a y with the property $G(x, y)$. Our primitive formula asserts that for every such x we can select one of the associated values of y so that the correspondence becomes single-valued (*i.e.* a many-one correspondence). F represents this single-valued correspondence.

Further, let $\mathfrak{A}(x, F(\ldots))$ be a formula which contains the free individual variable x and the free n-adic predicate variable F. Let $\mathfrak{A}(x, G(x, \ldots))$ signify the formula which is obtained from $\mathfrak{A}(x, F(\ldots))$ by replacing in it every partial expression $F(\mathfrak{a}_1, \mathfrak{a}_2, \ldots, \mathfrak{a}_n)$ by $G(x, \mathfrak{a}_1, \mathfrak{a}_2, \ldots, \mathfrak{a}_n)$ in accordance with Rule $a3$), where G is a predicate variable with $n + 1$ argument places. Then one can also take

h) $(x)(EF)\mathfrak{A}(x, F(\ldots))) \to (EG)(x)\mathfrak{A}(x, G(x, \ldots)))$

as a primitive formula. The truth of this formula may be seen as follows: If for every x there is an F such that $\mathfrak{A}(x, F(\ldots))$ holds, then for every x we can select one of these F's, which we shall call F^x. If we now define G so that

$(x)(y_1)(y_2)\ldots(y_n)[G(x, y_1, \ldots, y_n) \sim F^x(y_1, \ldots, y_n)]$

holds, then we have found a G of the kind postulated by the primitive formula h).

The rules of inference remain the same as in the restricted predicate calculus except that Rules $\gamma 1$), $\gamma 2$), and δ) are now to be extended so that they hold also for predicate variables.

Using this system we can carry over, with suitable modifications, results obtained earlier for the restricted predicate calculus. For example, the theorem about the prenex normal form, the Principle of Duality, and the theorem about the construction of the contradictory of a formula remain valid. Likewise, with any formula of the restricted predicate calculus containing individual variables there can be associated a class of formulas in which predicate variables occur. Thus to the fact that

$(x)(F(x) \to G(x)) \to ((Ex)F(x) \to (Ex)G(x))$

(Theorem 34) was a provable formula, there now corresponds the provability of every formula of the form

$(F)[\mathfrak{A}(F) \to \mathfrak{B}(F)] \to [(EF)\mathfrak{A}(F) \to (EF)\mathfrak{B}(F)].$

In the proof we need only repeat the proof of Theorem 34 with appropriate modifications. The same holds also for all other theorems of the restricted predicate calculus.

By the *decision problem* of the second order calculus, we understand the problem of deciding whether or not a given formula of the calculus is universally valid. In the stronger form, it would be a question of deciding for which domain of individuals the formula is a true sentence and for which it is not. Since the decision problem of the second order calculus includes that of the first order calculus, a general solution is *a fortiori* out of the question.

Apart from those cases belonging to the domain of the restricted predicate calculus and solved there, we have only one important special result, namely that the decision problem has been completely solved for the class of formulas containing only *monadic* predicates. The proof was given in the papers of Löwenheim, Skolem, and Behmann mentioned in § 12 of the preceding chapter. These contain the solution of the decision problem in the stronger sense.

For a detailed description of the decision procedure, we refer to the exceptionally lucid paper by Behmann. We shall, however, briefly outline the method used. The solution of the decision problem in the case of monadic predicates is based on the solution of the *problem of elimination* for this case. By the elimination problem in general, we mean the following: Let there be given a formula $\mathfrak{A}(F, G_1, \ldots, G_m, x_1, \ldots, x_k)$ which contains the free predicate variables $F, G_1, \ldots, G_m$ and in addition the free individual variables $x_1, x_2, \ldots, x_k$, and possibly bound individual variables as well, but no bound predicate variables. We then ask whether a formula $\mathfrak{B}(G_1, \ldots, G_m, x_1, \ldots, x_k)$, likewise containing no bound predicate variables, can be found such that

$$(F)\,\mathfrak{A}(F, G_1, \ldots, G_m, x_1, \ldots, x_k) \sim \mathfrak{B}(G_1, \ldots, G_m, x_1, \ldots, x_k)$$

or equivalently

$$(EF)\,\overline{\mathfrak{A}}(F, G_1, \ldots, G_m, x_1, \ldots, x_k) \sim \overline{\mathfrak{B}}(G_1, \ldots, G_m, x_1, \ldots, x_k)$$

is a universally valid formula of second order. If that is the case, then in each formula the component

$$(F)\,\mathfrak{A}\,(F, G_1, \ldots, G_m, x_1, \ldots, x_k)$$

or

$$(EF)\,\overline{\mathfrak{A}}\,(F, G_1, \ldots, G_m, x_1, \ldots, x_k)$$

can be replaced by

$$\mathfrak{B}\,(G_1, \ldots, G_m, x_1, \ldots, x_k)$$

or

$$\overline{\mathfrak{B}}\,(G_1, \ldots, G_m, x_1, \ldots, x_k)$$

respectively. Thus we can eliminate the predicate variable F in such a formula.

The relation to the decision problem is clear. Given a formula of the predicate calculus for which the decision is to be made, we first eliminate the free predicate variables by prefixing the appropriate universal quantifiers to the formula, and then, assuming we have a solution of the problem of elimination, eliminate the predicate variables one after the other, beginning from within, so that as a final result we obtain the value truth or the value falsehood or perhaps a condition on the number of individuals.

The reduction of formulas by elimination will be illustrated by the example of the formula

$$(F)\,\{(Ex)F(x)\,\text{v}\,(EG)\,[\,(x)\,(G(x) \sim \overline{F}(x))\,\&\,(x)G(x)\,]\,\}.$$

We note first that the formula

$$(EF)\,(x)\,(A(x)\,\text{v}\,F(x)\,\&\,B(x)\,\text{v}\,\overline{F}(x)) \sim (x)\,(A(x)\,\text{v}\,B(x)),$$

which constitutes a fundamental result for elimination, is a universally valid formula, since the left side of the equivalence can be transformed into

$$(EF)\,(x)\,\{(\overline{F}(x) \rightarrow A(x))\,\&\,(F(x) \rightarrow B(x))\,\}.$$

By means of this theorem we are able to eliminate the predicate variable G in our given formula. For we can replace the part

$$(x)\,(G(x) \sim \overline{F}(x))\,\&\,(x)G(x)$$

of the formula, constituting the scope of (EG), by

$$(x)\,(G(x)\,\text{v}\,F(x)\,\&\,\overline{G}(x)\,\text{v}\,\overline{F}(x)\,\&\,G(x))$$

in accordance with (29) of Chapter I, § 2 and Theorem 30 of Chapter III, § 6, or further by

$$(x)\,(G(x)\,\&\,\overline{F}(x)\,\mathrm{v}\,\overline{G}(x))$$

and finally by

$$(x)\,[\,(F(x)\,\&\,\overline{F}(x))\,\mathrm{v}\,G(x)\,\&\,\overline{F}(x)\,\mathrm{v}\,\overline{G}(x)\,].$$

Now, according to the above fundamental theorem for elimination,

$$(EG)\,(x)\,[\,(F(x)\,\&\,\overline{F}(x))\,\mathrm{v}\,G(x)\,\&\,\overline{F}(x)\,\mathrm{v}\,\overline{G}(x)\,]$$
$$\sim\,(x)\,[\,(F(x)\,\&\,\overline{F}(x))\,\mathrm{v}\,\overline{F}(x)\,]$$

is valid. Also,

$$(x)\,[\,(F(x)\,\&\,\overline{F}(x))\,\mathrm{v}\,\overline{F}(x)\,]$$

can be replaced by $(x)\overline{F}(x)$. Thus our original formula

$$(F)\,\{\,(Ex)F(x)\,\mathrm{v}\,(EG)\,[\,(x)\,(G(x)\,\sim\,\overline{F}(x))\,\&\,(x)G(x)\,]\,\},$$

after elimination of the predicate variable G, is transformed into

$$(F)\,\{\,(Ex)F(x)\,\mathrm{v}\,(x)\overline{F}(x)\,\}.$$

This last formula, in which the scope of (F) has the form $\mathfrak{A}\,\mathrm{v}\,\overline{\mathfrak{A}}$, enables us to recognize immediately that our original formula is universally valid.

As already noted above, the elimination problem can be completely solved if none but monadic predicates occur. Since the method of elimination constitutes the only method which applies with any generality to the treatment of the decision problem, we are led to search for an elimination procedure which will work also for formulas containing predicates with two or more argument places. In fact, for formulas having certain special structures, it is actually possible to carry out the elimination. Numerous isolated results of this sort are to be found in the third volume of Ernst Schröder's "Vorlesungen über die Algebra der Logik." Unfortunately, however, it can be shown that there are formulas in which an elimination result in the above sense does not exist, so that in the general case the whole elimination problem must be given a more comprehensive formulation.[1] The relation to the decision problem is more involved in that case.

---

[1] Cf. W. Ackermann, *Untersuchungen über das Eliminationsproblem der mathematischen Logik.* Math. Ann. Vol. 110 (1934).—*Zum Eliminationsproblem der mathematischen Logik.* Math. Ann. Vol. 111 (1935).

§ 2. Introduction of Predicates of Second Level; Logical Treatment of the Number Concept

For the intuitive interpretation on which we have hitherto based the predicate calculus, it was essential that the sentences and predicates should be sharply differentiated from the individuals, which occur as the argument values of the predicates. Now, however, there is nothing to prevent us from *considering the predicates and sentences themselves as individuals which may serve as arguments of predicates.*

Consider, for example, a logical expression of the form $(x)(A \to F(x))$. This may be interpreted as a predicate $P(A, F)$ whose first argument place is occupied by a sentence A, and whose second argument place is occupied by a monadic predicate F.

A false sentence A is related to every F by the relation $P(A, F)$; a true sentence A only to those F for which $(x)F(x)$ holds.

Further examples are given by the properties of *reflexivity, symmetry,* and *transitivity* of dyadic predicates. To these correspond three predicates: $\mathrm{Ref}(R)$, $\mathrm{Sym}(R)$, and $\mathrm{Tr}(R)$, whose argument R is a dyadic predicate. These three properties are expressed in symbols as follows:

$$\mathrm{Ref}(R): \quad (x)R(x, x),$$
$$\mathrm{Sym}(R): \quad (x)(y)(R(x, y) \to R(y, x)),$$
$$\mathrm{Tr}(R): \quad (x)(y)(z)(R(x, y) \,\&\, R(y, z) \to R(x, z)).$$

All three properties are possessed by the predicate $\equiv(x, y)$ (x is identical with y). The predicate $<(x, y)$, on the other hand, possesses only the property of transitivity. Thus the formulas $\mathrm{Ref}(\equiv)$, $\mathrm{Sym}(\equiv)$, $\mathrm{Tr}(\equiv)$, and $\mathrm{Tr}(<)$ are true sentences, whereas $\mathrm{Ref}(<)$ and $\mathrm{Sym}(<)$ are false.

Such *predicates of predicates* will be called *predicates of second level.*

An example of a dyadic predicate of second level is furnished by *Equivalence,* $\mathrm{Eq}(F, G)$, which is defined by the expression $(x)(F(x) \sim G(x))$, and which means that the predicates F and G both hold or both fail to hold for any given argument value. Some other dyadic predicates of second level are: *Incompatibility,*

Inc (F, G), and *Implication*, Imp (F, G), which are defined symbolically by:

$$(x) (\overline{F}(x) \vee \overline{G}(x))$$

and

$$(x) (F(x) \to G(x))$$

respectively.

These considerations still do not lead to an actual extension of the symbolism, since the above predicates of second level can be expressed in the calculus we have been using and since such formulas as Ref (R) and Sym (R) are to be regarded as mere abbreviations. We obtain our first real extension by introducing variables for predicates of second level, of which the above predicate constants are special values. For a while we shall employ such variables only occasionally, because the systematic development of this second extension of the calculus will not come until later. In this and in the following section we merely wish to convince ourselves of the advantages which result from the introduction of predicates of second level.

The first important application is furnished by the *logical investigation of the concept of number*. A number is not an individual in the proper sense of the word, but a property. The individuals to which number applies as a property cannot be the counted things themselves, since each of these is but one thing, so that a number different from 1 could not possibly occur in this way. However, number may be considered to be a property of that concept under which the selected individuals are united. For example, the fact that the number of continents is five cannot be expressed by saying that each continent has the number five as a property; but it is a property of the predicate "to be a continent" that it holds for exactly five individuals.

Numbers thus appear as the properties of predicates, and in our calculus *every number is represented as a predicate constant of second level*. The importance of this representation of numbers is based on the fact that the second-level predicate constants which represent numbers may be expressed entirely in terms of the logical symbols. Thus it becomes possible to subsume the theory of numbers under logic. We give here the expressions for the numbers 0, 1, and 2, *i.e.* for the second-level predicates $0(F)$, $1(F)$, and $2(F)$:

$$0(F) : \quad \overline{(Ex)}F(x).$$

("There is no x for which F is true.")

$$1(F) : \quad (Ex)[F(x) \& (y)(F(y) \to \equiv (x, y))].$$

("There is an x for which $F(x)$ holds, and any y for which $F(y)$ holds is identical with this x.")

$$2(F) : \quad (Ex)(Ey)\{\overline{\equiv}(x, y) \& F(x) \& F(y) \& (z)$$
$$[F(z) \to \equiv (x, z) \text{ v} \equiv (y, z)]\}.$$

("There are two different x and y for which F is true, and any z for which $F(z)$ holds is identical either with x or with y.")

The numerical equivalence of two predicates F and G may be regarded as a second-level predicate constant $\text{Ne}(F, G)$. The numerical equivalence of F and G means nothing other than that the individuals for which F holds may be put into one-to-one correspondence with the individuals for which G holds. Consequently, $\text{Ne}(F, G)$ may be defined by the following expression:

$$(ER)\{(x)[F(x) \to (Ey)(R(x, y) \& G(y))]$$
$$\& (y)[G(y) \to (Ex)(R(x, y) \& F(x))]$$
$$\& (x)(y)(z)[(R(x, y) \& R(x, z) \to \equiv (y, z))$$
$$\& (R(x, z) \& R(y, z) \to \equiv (x, y))]\}.$$

The addition of numbers may be reduced to the disjunction of predicates. In fact, if F and G are incompatible predicates and if the number m is associated with the predicate F and the number n with the predicate G, then the number $m + n$ corresponds to the predicate F v G.

On the basis of this concept of addition, numerical equations such as:

$$1 + 1 = 2, \quad 2 + 3 = 5$$

become purely logical, provable formulas. For example, the equation $1 + 1 = 2$ is rendered by the logical formula:

$$(F)(G)\{[\text{Inc}(F, G) \& 1(F) \& 1(G)] \to 2(F \text{ v } G)\},$$

whose universal validity is obvious if the defining expressions are substituted for the second-level predicate Inc as well as for the second-level predicates 1 and 2.

The general concept of number may also be set up by means of our logical tools. If a predicate $\Phi(F)$ of the second level is to represent a number, then Φ must satisfy the following conditions:

For two numerically equivalent predicates F and G, Φ must hold either for both or for neither. For two predicates F and G which are not numerically equivalent, Φ is to hold for at most one of them.

Formally, these conditions on Φ are expressed thus:

$$(F)(G)\{[\Phi(F) \& \Phi(G) \to \mathrm{Ne}(F, G)]$$
$$\& [\Phi(F) \& \mathrm{Ne}(F, G) \to \Phi(G)]\}.$$

The entire expression represents a property of Φ. Thus if for abbreviation we denote this property by $\mathfrak{N}(\Phi)$, then we can say:

A number is a second-level predicate which has the property $\mathfrak{N}(\Phi)$.

A difficulty will appear if we attempt to state the condition under which two second-level predicates Φ and Ψ with the properties $\mathfrak{N}(\Phi)$ and $\mathfrak{N}(\Psi)$ define the same number. This condition consists in that $\Phi(P)$ and $\Psi(P)$ either both hold or both do not hold for any given predicate P, *i.e.* that the following relation obtains:

$$(P)(\Phi(P) \sim \Psi(P)).$$

Now let us assume that our domain of individuals consists of a finite number of individuals. Then we have the unfortunate situation that all numbers greater than the number of individuals in the domain are equal according to our definition. For if the number of individuals is less than, say, 10^{60}, and we take for Φ and Ψ the predicates which define the numbers 10^{60} and $10^{60} + 1$, then neither Ψ nor Φ applies to any predicate P. The relation

$$(P)(\Phi(P) \sim \Psi(P))$$

is thus satisfied for Φ and Ψ, *i.e.*, Φ and Ψ would represent the same number.

To avoid this difficulty, the domain of individuals must be assumed to be infinite. In so doing, however, we forego a logical proof of the existence of an infinite totality.

It is also of particular interest to observe how the axioms of number theory become provable theorems of logic when we take as our basis the logical introduction of the number concept and make use—essential use, to be sure—of the axiom of infinity referred to above. We cannot here enter into this in any detail.[1] The above remarks are only to give some idea of the applicability of the extended calculus.

§ 3. Representation of the Fundamental Concepts of Set Theory in the Extended Calculus

As early as in the second chapter it was evident that set theory and mathematical logic are intimately related. We were able to interpret the same logical formulas at will as expressing relations between classes or between monadic predicates, without different logical connections being involved in the two interpretations. Here, also, it will be possible to interpret as set-theoretic relations the logical connections which are expressible in our calculus.

In order to examine this relation more thoroughly, we shall first of all take a closer look at the relation between predicates in the restricted sense, i.e., monadic predicates, and sets. A set either is given by enumeration of its elements or is defined as the system of all those things for which some definite predicate holds. The first method of determining a set is possible only for finite sets and need not be examined further. For, every set obtained by enumeration of its elements can also be defined by means of a predicate. For example, a set consisting of three individuals a, b, and c may be defined as the set of all those objects x for which the predicate

$$\equiv (x, a) \; \mathrm{v} \equiv (x, b) \; \mathrm{v} \equiv (x, c)$$

holds.

---

[1] For a detailed and easily understandable treatment of this question, consult B. Russell, *Introduction to Mathematical Philosophy*.

Accordingly, we now think of every set as being defined by a predicate. We must note at this point that every predicate determines uniquely its corresponding set, *i.e.* the set of individuals for which it holds, but that to a given set there does not belong only *one* defining predicate; rather, a set may be defined by predicates in various ways. Thus the set of all equilateral triangles is the same as the set of all equiangular triangles. To give another example, not from mathematics: The set of ruminants now living coincides with the set of ungulates with cleft hoofs.

The necessary and sufficient condition for two predicates P and Q to determine the same set consists in the equivalence of the two predicates, that is, in their satisfying the relation $\mathrm{Eq}(P, Q)$, *i.e.* $(x)(P(x) \sim Q(x))$. In the sense of set theory, therefore, the predicate of second level $\mathrm{Eq}(P, Q)$ is nothing but the identity of P and Q.

Just as predicates may be regarded as designating sets, so may a monadic predicate $F(P)$ of second level be interpreted as designating a property of sets.

In order for this interpretation to be possible, it is necessary that the truth or falsehood of F for a predicate P be uniquely determined by the set corresponding to P; and, according to the above, the condition for this is simultaneous truth or falsehood of the sentences associated with equivalent predicates by the second-level predicate F. Thus, in symbols, we must have the relation

$$(P)(Q)\{\mathrm{Eq}(P, Q) \to (F(P) \to F(Q))\}$$

for the predicate F, which we abbreviate by $\mathfrak{M}(F)$.

This condition is satisfied, for example, by predicates of second level which represent numbers. It is because of this property of numbers that they may also be regarded as predicates of sets. The interpretation of numbers as properties of sets, as opposed to their interpretation as properties of predicates, has the advantage that it makes self-evident the invariance of number under replacement of a predicate by an equivalent one.

From the relation between sets and predicates there follows further a connection between sets of sets and predicates of second level. Every set of sets is defined by a property characteristic of all its constituent sets.

Let us now take two predicates of sets, *i.e.*, two predicates of second level, $F(P)$ and $G(P)$, which satisfy the condition $\mathfrak{M}(F)$ and $\mathfrak{M}(G)$. To these two set-predicates F and G corresponds the same set of sets if F and G both apply or both do not apply to the same sets. The relation $(P)(F(P) \sim G(P))$ accordingly means that the set of sets corresponding to F is the same as that corresponding to G.

The set-theoretic interpretation of the extended predicate calculus may also be extended to n-adic predicates. Every predicate $R(x, y)$ selects from the set of all possible pairs (x, y) a certain set of ordered pairs, namely the set of those pairs (x, y) for which $R(x, y)$ holds. In the case of two predicates R_1 and R_2, the sets corresponding to them are identical if the relation $\mathrm{Eq}(R_1, R_2)$, *i.e.* $(x)(y)(R_1(x, y) \sim R_2(x, y))$, holds. If it is to be possible for a second-level predicate $F(R)$ to be interpreted as a predicate of the two sets, then it must satisfy the relation

$$(R_1)(R_2)\{\mathrm{Eq}(R_1, R_2) \to (F(R_1) \to F(R_2))\}.$$

Similarly for predicates with three or more argument places.

From this we see that the extended calculus admits of a set-theoretic interpretation just as well as of a purely logical interpretation. The theory of numbers may be treated entirely in the sense of the set-theoretic interpretation. We have already seen that the predicates of second level (*i.e.*, predicates of predicates) which define numbers can just as well be regarded as predicates of sets. Moreover, we mentioned above that two predicates of second level $\Phi(P)$ and $\Psi(P)$ which represent numbers give the same number if the relation

$$(P)(\Phi(P) \sim \Psi(P))$$

holds for Φ and Ψ.

From this it follows, however, that numbers may be regarded also as sets of sets. In the logical definition, a number was a predicate of second level which holds for all numerically equivalent predicates and only for these. To numerical equivalence of predicates corresponds the equivalence of sets (equivalence to be understood here in the usual set-theoretic sense). From the logical concept of numbers one thus gets to a set-theoretic one according to which a number is nothing but the set of all sets equivalent to a given set.

We shall now see how the usual concepts of set theory can be constructed in the symbolism of our calculus.

If $P_1(x)$ and $P_2(x)$ are the defining predicates of two sets, then the *union* of these two sets is given by the predicate $P_1(x) \vee P_2(x)$. $P_1(x) \& P_2(x)$ represents the *intersection* of P_1 and P_2. The set P_1 is contained in P_2, or P_1 is a *subset* of P_2, if $(x)(P_1(x) \to P_2(x))$ is a true statement. Two sets P_1 and P_2 are *equivalent* if the elements of one of the sets may be put into one-to-one correspondence with the elements of the other. The symbolic expression for this is the same as that for the numerical equivalence of predicates.

The expression

$$(x)(y)(z)\left([R(x, y) \& R(x, z) \to \;\equiv (y, z)]\right.$$
$$\left. \& [R(x, z) \& R(y, z) \to \;\equiv (x, y)]\right)$$

or, abbreviated, Sgl(R) means that the relation $R(x, y)$, when it holds, is single-valued both ways. The symbolic expression for the (set-theoretic) equivalence of P_1 and P_2 is then:

$$(ER)\{(x)[P_1(x) \to (Ey)(R(x, y) \& P_2(y))]$$
$$\& (y)[P_2(y) \to (Ex)(R(x, y) \& P_1(x))] \& \text{Sgl}(R)\}.$$

The *set of all subsets* of a given set defined by D is represented by a certain second-level predicate Sb(P) (or, better, Sb(P, D)). Every predicate P for which Sb(P) holds must have the property that all of its elements are also elements of D. Conversely, Sb(P) must hold for every such predicate P. Hence, Sb(P) is defined by the expression:

$$(x)(P(x) \to D(x)).$$

Furthermore, let $F(P)$ represent any set of sets. The elements x of the *union of this set of sets* may be characterized by each being an element of at least one set belonging to P for which $F(P)$ holds. Hence we obtain as the defining expression for the union:

$$(EP)\,(F(P)\,\&\,P(x))\,.$$

The elements of the *intersection of the set of sets* are characterized by each being an element of every set P for which $F(P)$ holds. Hence the intersection is represented by

$$(P)\,(F(P) \to P(x))\,.$$

A set P is called *ordered* if for the elements of P there is defined a dyadic predicate R which is transitive but not reflexive and which for any two different x and y holds either for the pair (x, y) or for the pair (y, x). "The set P is ordered by the predicate R," is thus expressed symbolically by:

$$(x)\,(y)\,(z)\,\{\,[P(x)\,\&\,P(y)\,\&\,P(z)] \to [\overline{R}(x, x)$$
$$\&\,(\equiv(x, y)\,\mathrm{v}\,R(x, y)\,\mathrm{v}\,R(y, x))$$
$$\&\,(R(x, y)\,\&\,R(y, z) \to R(x, z))]\,\}\,.$$

We abbreviate this formula by the symbol $\mathfrak{O}(P, R)$.

The set P is said to be *well-ordered* by the predicate R, if

$$\mathfrak{O}(P, R)\,\&\,(Q)\,\{\,(x)\,(Q(x) \to P(x)) \to (Ey)$$
$$[Q(y)\,\&\,(z)\,(Q(z) \to \equiv(y, z)\,\mathrm{v}\,R(y, z))]\,\}$$
is a true statement.

In a similar way all the remaining concepts of set theory may be represented in the symbolism of our calculus.

§ 4. The Logical Paradoxes

In the previous sections we have seen what new possibilities of expression result from the introduction of predicates of second level. Every formula containing a free predicate variable F can be regarded as a second-level predicate constant. Further, we may introduce variables for second-level predicates. A formula containing a free variable of this sort defines a predicate constant whose arguments are predicates of second level, and so forth. This construction may be continued indefinitely.

Thus, in addition to the objects of the domain of individuals, we may also have predicates, second-level predicates, and so forth, as individuals in an extended sense. The question now arises whether we can, without more ado, unite these individuals in the extended sense to form a single new domain of individuals, so that besides speaking of predicates of individuals, predicates of these predicates, ..., predicates of the n-th level, etc., we can also speak simply of predicates, and so that every predicate for the new domain of individuals belongs itself to the domain of individuals. In this case, a predicate would have to be capable of containing itself also as argument. And the concept of second-level predicate etc. would have to be set up with a similar generality.

The way in which we have arrived at predicates of a higher level, beginning as we did with the restricted predicate calculus, will be of no help in any such attempt. This is because the discussion of the preceding section was entirely concerned with predicates of individuals, predicates of such first-level predicates, etc. It is true, however, that such a general concept of predicate corresponds to the imprecise usage of speech.[1] It will quickly become apparent that such a logical system does not even satisfy the condition of being consistent. The contradictions which occur, the so-called *paradoxes*, which, incidentally, we encounter whether or not we use logical symbolism, can be given a set-theoretic interpretation, or a logical interpretation proper, depending on which of the two interpretations of the predicate calculus we use. A few of these contradictions will be described here.

Let $P(F)$ be a predicate of second level. Since P itself is a predicate, the expression $P(P)$ stands for a sentence which may be true or false. An example of a second-level predicate such that $P(P)$ stands for a true sentence is furnished by the negation of the predicate $0(F)$ ("F holds for no individual"), *i.e.*, the function $\bar{0}(F)$, which is defined by the expression $(Ex)F(x)$. $\bar{0}(\bar{0})$ is an abbreviation for $(EF)\bar{0}(F)$, which in turn may be written as $(EF)(Ex)F(x)$. The last formula indeed expresses a true statement, namely, "There is a predicate F and an individual x such that $F(x)$ holds."

---

[1] In the set-theoretic interpretation of our calculus, this corresponds to the naïve point of view in set theory.

On the other hand, $0(0)$ is a false sentence. For, by the definition of 0, we obtain

$$0(0) \sim \overline{(EF)}\,[0(F)] \sim \overline{(EF)}\,\overline{(Ex)}\,F(x) \sim (F)\,(Ex)\,F(x).$$

The last expression stands for the false sentence to the effect that every predicate holds for at least one individual.

Now we may regard the expression $P(P)$ as a predicate of P. This predicate expresses the property of the predicate P that it applies to itself. We shall symbolize this new predicate of predicates by $Pd(P)$ (read "P is predicable"). Since Pd, and thus also $\overline{Pd}$, is a predicate of a predicate, the expressions $Pd(\overline{Pd})$ and $\overline{Pd}(\overline{Pd})$ also have meaning. Now either $\overline{Pd}(\overline{Pd})$ is true, *i.e.* the predicate $\overline{Pd}$ applies to itself, in which case $Pd(\overline{Pd})$ is true; or else $\overline{Pd}(\overline{Pd})$ is not true, *i.e.*, the predicate $\overline{Pd}$ does not apply to itself, in which case $Pd(\overline{Pd})$ is true. Consequently, it follows that

$$Pd(\overline{Pd}) \sim \overline{Pd}(\overline{Pd}).$$

This, however, is a contradiction, for a logical expression can never be equivalent to its contradictory.

This paradox was first discovered by Russell. It may also be expressed in the terminology of the theory of sets. Here the set of all sets which are not elements of themselves corresponds to the predicate Pd. The very concept of this set is self-contradictory, for by its definition it is an element of itself if and only if it is not an element of itself.

The second of the paradoxes to be discussed was already known in Greek philosophy. Its simplest formulation is the following: Suppose someone says, "I am lying," or more explicitly, "I am now asserting a falsehood." Then this sentence is true if it is false and false if it is true.

Let us formulate this paradox in a somewhat more precise way. Let $\mathfrak{P}$ designate some definite person and let t be the abbreviated notation for some definite time-interval. Within this time-interval t, let $\mathfrak{P}$ make the statement, "Everything said by $\mathfrak{P}$ in the time-interval t is false"; and let $\mathfrak{P}$ say nothing further during the time t. This assumption is certainly not contradictory, since its realization may be deliberately brought about. In order to express it in the logical symbolism, let us designate by $\mathfrak{A}$ the above statement made by $\mathfrak{P}$, and use the predicate sign $\mathrm{As}(X)$ to mean, "X is asserted by $\mathfrak{P}$ in the time-interval t," where any sentence may be taken as a value of the argument X.

By means of this sign we can, to begin with, render the statement $\mathfrak{A}$ by the formula

$$(X) (\mathrm{As}(X) \to \overline{X}) \ ;$$

and our assumption that $\mathfrak{P}$ makes the statement $\mathfrak{A}$, and nothing else, within the time-interval t, may be expressed by the two formulas

$$\mathrm{As}(\mathfrak{A}) \quad \text{and} \quad (X) [\mathrm{As}(X) \to \ \equiv (\mathfrak{A}, X)] .$$

Now a contradiction is brought about as follows. In the valid formula $\mathfrak{A} \to \mathfrak{A}$, we replace $\mathfrak{A}$ on the right by the expression $(X) (\mathrm{As}(X) \to \overline{X})$, which constitutes the symbolic rendering of the sentence $\mathfrak{A}$. Then we obtain

$$\mathfrak{A} \to (X) (\mathrm{As}(X) \to \overline{X}) .$$

The universal quantifier (X) can here be left out by the rules of our calculus, yielding

$$\mathfrak{A} \to (\mathrm{As}(X) \to \overline{X}) .$$

By substitution we obtain from this

$$\mathfrak{A} \to (\mathrm{As}(\mathfrak{A}) \to \overline{\mathfrak{A}}) .$$

Since the antecedents in the implications can be interchanged, the last formula can be replaced by

$$\mathrm{As}(\mathfrak{A}) \to (\mathfrak{A} \to \overline{\mathfrak{A}}) .$$

Since $\mathrm{As}(\mathfrak{A})$ is a true formula, we obtain

$$\mathfrak{A} \to \overline{\mathfrak{A}} .$$

On the other hand, $\overline{\mathfrak{A}} \to \mathfrak{A}$ may also be proved. For we have first

$$\overline{\mathfrak{A}} \to (\overline{X}) (\mathrm{As}(X) \to \overline{X}) ,$$

hence

$$\overline{\mathfrak{A}} \to (EX) (\mathrm{As}(X) \ \& \ X) .$$

Further, there follows from the formula

$$(X) (\text{As}(X) \to \, \equiv (\mathfrak{A}, X)),$$

which was assumed true, that

$$(X) (\text{As}(X) \, \& \, X \to \, \equiv (\mathfrak{A}, X) \, \& \, X),$$

and from this

$$(EX) (\text{As}(X) \, \& \, X) \to (EX) (\equiv (\mathfrak{A}, X) \, \& \, X),$$

so that we obtain

$$\overline{\mathfrak{A}} \to (EX) (\equiv (\mathfrak{A}, X) \, \& \, X).$$

Now, by the meaning of identity, $\equiv (\mathfrak{A}, X) \, \& \, X \to \mathfrak{A}$ is a true formula. From this we have, by Rule $\gamma)$:

$$(EX) (\equiv (\mathfrak{A}, X) \, \& \, X) \to \mathfrak{A}.$$

This formula in conjunction with the one obtained just before yields

$$\overline{\mathfrak{A}} \to \mathfrak{A}.$$

However, from the formulas $\mathfrak{A} \to \overline{\mathfrak{A}}$ and $\overline{\mathfrak{A}} \to \mathfrak{A}$, which we have proved, it follows that both $\mathfrak{A}$ and $\overline{\mathfrak{A}}$ are true formulas, so that we have indeed arrived at a contradiction.

We shall now give a third paradox, of which there are many different versions. A simple way of presenting it is the following: Any act of designating a number, whether by communication of a conventional symbol or by statement of a property defining this number, takes a certain minimum amount of time. Therefore, a finite number of men can name only finitely many numbers in a finite amount of time. On the other hand, there are infinitely many numbers. From this it follows with certainty that not all numbers will be named by men living on earth during the twentieth century. Among the numbers not named in the twentieth century there is a smallest. Now, however, this number has been named in the twentieth century after all, for we have defined it by the property of being the smallest number not named in the twentieth century. Thus there results the existence of a number which is named as well as not named.

In order to make this argument somewhat more precise for the purpose of symbolic rendition in our calculus, let us replace the concept of naming by a more restricted concept. Let us consider only such names of a number as can be given in the sense of our logical symbolism by the writing out of an expression for a predicate which defines the number. Here we understand by a predicate defining the number x one which holds for the number x but for nothing else.[1] In this way, we arrive at the following formulation of the paradox:

Let $\text{Scr}(P)$ signify the property of a predicate P that at least one of the expressions written in logical symbols during the twentieth century is an expression for P. Let the symbol $<(x, y)$ be used, as before, for the predicate "x is less than y," where the argument places of this predicate refer to the positive integers as their domain of individuals.

Furthermore, the expression

$$P(x) \mathbin{\&} (y) \big(P(y) \to \;\equiv (x, y)\big),$$

which says that x is defined by the predicate P, will be abbreviated by $\text{Df}(P, x)$. The symbol $\text{Dsc}(x)$ will be used to abbreviate

$$(EP)(\text{Df}(P, x) \mathbin{\&} \text{Scr}(P)).$$

Thus $\text{Dsc}(x)$ means, "Among the symbolic expressions written during the twentieth century, at least one constitutes a predicate which defines x," or more briefly, "x is defined symbolically at least once during the twentieth century." Finally, as an abbreviation for the expression

$$\overline{\text{Dsc}(x)} \mathbin{\&} (y) \big(<(y, x) \to \text{Dsc}(y)\big),$$

we will use the symbol $\text{Lst}(x)$ so that accordingly $\text{Lst}(x)$ means "x has the property of being the least number not defined symbolically during the twentieth century."

---

[1] That numbers may be regarded as predicates of second level need not be taken into account in the present argument.

We now introduce the following formulas as axioms. First, the expressions for the basic properties of the relation $< (x, y)$:

$$(x) \overline{< (x, x)},$$
$$(x)\,(y)\,(z)\,(< (x, y) \;\&\; < (y, z) \to < (x, z)),$$
$$(x)\,(y)\,[\equiv (x, y) \;\mathrm{v}\; < (x, y) \;\mathrm{v}\; < (y, x)],$$
$$(Ex)P(x) \to (Ex)\,[P(x) \;\&\; (y)\,(< (y, x) \to \overline{P}(y))].$$

Of these four axioms, the first three mean that the relation $< (x, y)$ *orders* the whole numbers; and the last, that they are *well-ordered*. We next take as an axiom the symbolic expression for the fact that not all numbers can be defined symbolically in the twentieth century,

$$(Ex) \overline{\mathrm{Dsc}}(x),$$

and finally the formula Scr (Lst), which says that an expression for Lst (x) has been written down in the twentieth century, and which, therefore, is true, since we have written above an expression for Lst (x).

Now we can proceed with the following formal argument. In the formula

$$(Ex)P(x) \to (Ex)\,[P(x) \;\&\; (y)\,(< (y, x) \to \overline{P}(y))],$$

we substitute $\overline{\mathrm{Dsc}}$ for P and obtain

$$(Ex) \overline{\mathrm{Dsc}}(x) \to (Ex)\,[\overline{\mathrm{Dsc}}(x) \;\&\; (y)\,(< (y, x) \to \mathrm{Dsc}(y))].$$

Since $(Ex) \overline{\mathrm{Dsc}}(x)$ is true, we obtain

$$(Ex)\,[\overline{\mathrm{Dsc}}(x) \;\&\; (y)\,(< (y, x) \to \mathrm{Dsc}(y))] \;;$$

hence if we use the abbreviation Lst (x), we obtain

$$(Ex)\,\mathrm{Lst}(x).$$

By definition of Lst, the relation

$$\mathrm{Lst}(x) \to \overline{\mathrm{Dsc}}(x)$$

holds. Furthermore, by means of the above axioms we can derive the formula

$$\mathrm{Lst}(x) \to \mathrm{Lst}(x) \;\&\; (y)\,(\mathrm{Lst}(y) \to \equiv (x, y)),$$

that is,

$$\mathrm{Lst}(x) \to \mathrm{Df}(\mathrm{Lst}, x).$$

From the last and second from last formulas, we obtain

$$\text{Lst}(x) \to \overline{\text{Dsc}(x)} \,\&\, \text{Df}(\text{Lst}, x).$$

By the rule associated with Theorem 34, we obtain further:

$$(Ex)\,\text{Lst}(x) \to (Ex)\,(\overline{\text{Dsc}(x)} \,\&\, \text{Df}(\text{Lst}, x)).$$

Since $(Ex)\,\text{Lst}(x)$ is proved, the Rule of Implication gives

$$(Ex)\,(\overline{\text{Dsc}(x)} \,\&\, \text{Df}(\text{Lst}, x)).$$

If one adds to this formula $\text{Scr}(\text{Lst})$, which was taken as an axiom, there results

$$(Ex)\,\{\overline{\text{Dsc}(x)} \,\&\, \text{Df}(\text{Lst}, x) \,\&\, \text{Scr}(\text{Lst})\}.$$

Now the formula

$$F(Q) \to (EP)F(P)$$

holds by Axiom f).

If we now replace Q by Lst and $F(P)$ by

$$(Ex)\,\{\overline{\text{Dsc}(x)} \,\&\, \text{Df}(P, x) \,\&\, \text{Scr}(P)\},$$

we obtain

$$(Ex)\,\{\overline{\text{Dsc}(x)} \,\&\, \text{Df}(\text{Lst}, x) \,\&\, \text{Scr}(\text{Lst})\}$$
$$\to (EP)\,(Ex)\,\{\overline{\text{Dsc}(x)} \,\&\, \text{Df}(P, x) \,\&\, \text{Scr}(P)\};$$

hence, since the antecedent is a formula already proved, we have

$$(EP)\,(Ex)\,\{\overline{\text{Dsc}(x)} \,\&\, \text{Df}(P, x) \,\&\, \text{Scr}(P)\}.$$

Since the quantifiers may be interchanged, and since

$$(EP)\,(A \,\&\, F(P)) \sim A \,\&\, (EP)F(P),$$

we obtain

$$(Ex)\,\{\overline{\text{Dsc}(x)} \,\&\, (EP)\,(\text{Df}(P, x) \,\&\, \text{Scr}(P))\}.$$

By use of the abbreviation "Dsc," this expression is transformed into

$$(Ex)\,(\overline{\text{Dsc}(x)} \,\&\, \text{Dsc}(x)).$$

On the other hand, the formula

$$(x)\,(\text{Dsc}(x) \,\text{v}\, \overline{\text{Dsc}(x)})$$

can also be proved, for it is obtained from Theorem 21 by substitution. By the Principle of Duality, however, the last two formulas are contradictions of each other. We have thus a contradiction.

It is not possible to tolerate these various contradictions by accepting as a fact the provability of certain mutually contradictory sentences. For as soon as we admit any two mutually contradictory expressions $\mathfrak{A}$ and $\overline{\mathfrak{A}}$ as true formulas, the entire calculus becomes meaningless, as we have observed previously.

Let us now see what the paradoxes imply for the structure of our calculus. The first paradox shows clearly that we cannot employ an undifferentiated predicate concept of the sort described at the beginning of this section, since its admission would lead to a contradiction within the predicate calculus. The other two paradoxes, which were included here merely for the sake of completeness, have a different character. They show only the incompatibility of certain assertions. In the first case, these were

$$\text{As}[(X)(\text{As}(X) \to \overline{X})]$$

and

$$(X)\{\text{As}(X) \to \,\equiv\!(X, (Y)[\text{As}(Y) \to \overline{Y}]\,\textbf{)}\};$$

in the second case, they were

$$(Ex)\overline{\text{Dsc}(x)}, \quad \text{Scr}(\text{Lst}),$$

and

$$(P)\{(Ex)P(x) \to (Ex)[P(x) \,\&\, (y)(<(y, x) \to P(y))]\}.$$

None of these assertions is a universally valid formula. Hence the paradoxes of this second type, which are usually called "*semantical paradoxes*," do not even affect our calculus, since the calculus is incapable of expressing their purely logical character. For their partial formalization we rather had to rely upon the intuitive meaning of the concepts involved. Hence contradictions of the latter type do not force us to draw any conclusions regarding our predicate calculus, and we will therefore not go into them any further.[1]

---

[1] For a new treatment of the semantical paradoxes, cf., for example, A. Tarski, *Der Wahrheitsbegriff in den formalisierten Sprachen*, Studia Philosophica, (Lwow 1935). [English translation *in prep.*]

§ 5. The Predicate Calculus of Order ω

We shall now build up systematically the calculus as extended by the introduction of predicates of higher level. The considerations of the preceding section have shown us that we cannot use an undifferentiated concept of predicate, but that we must differentiate the predicates according to the kind of arguments they have. This will be reflected in our calculus in the formal conventions of using a common predicate variable only for predicates of the same type.

We have, first, predicates of individuals, and these are classified into predicates of different categories, or types, according to the number of their argument places. Such predicates are called *predicates of first level*.

By a *predicate of second level*, we understand one whose argument places are occupied by names of individuals or by predicates of first level, where a predicate of first level must occur at least once as an argument. The categories, or types, of predicates of second level are differentiated according to the number and kind of their argument places. Correspondingly, one arrives further at predicates of *third level, fourth level, etc.* For individual variables, we again use small italic letters; for the predicate variables, capital italic letters. For every predicate variable introduced, its type must be specified to start with, since the rules of substitution will be so formulated as to allow only predicates of the same type as a given variable to be substituted for this variable.

We may use a simple symbolism to specify the type of a predicate variable. We designate the type of an individual variable by i. If we have an n-adic predicate variable and if the arguments belonging to it are of types $a_1, a_2, \ldots, a_n$, then $(a_1, a_2, \ldots, a_n)$ is to designate the type of the predicate variable. For example, $((i, i), i)$ indicates the type of a dyadic predicate of second level in which the first argument may be any dyadic predicate of individuals and the second argument, the name of any individual. Of the predicates discussed in § 2 of this chapter, Sym has the type $((i, i))$; $0(F)$ the type $((i))$; $\mathfrak{R}(\Phi)$ the type $(((i)))$; Imp the type $((i), (i))$; etc.

This hierarchical ordering of predicates and the calculus based upon it was introduced into logic by Whitehead and Russell in their fundamental work *Principia Mathematica*. Besides the differentiation of types of predicates described here, the so-called *simple theory of types,* these authors employ a still finer classification of predicates, the *ramified theory of types.* In this latter theory, one is, for example, no longer allowed to consider all monadic predicates of individuals as belonging to a single type, but such predicates must be differentiated according to their mode of definition. For example, a predicate of individuals into whose definition quantifiers for predicates enter has to be of a higher type than the predicates of individuals of lowest order, called "predicative" predicates of individuals by Whitehead and Russell. This ramified theory of types was designed to take into account the semantical paradoxes. However, the theory is unnecessary, since this sort of contradiction, as we have seen, does not concern the extended predicate calculus. Besides, it entails a great number of difficulties, which were discussed at some length in the first edition of the present text. We no longer have any reason to consider this theory in any more detail, especially since the consistency of the simple calculus of order ω can be established without difficulty.

If we now turn to the details of the construction of the calculus of order ω, we encounter certain difficulties of notation. Up to now we have always expressed the fact that a predicate holds for certain arguments by writing the arguments, separated by commas, within a parenthesis following the predicate sign. This notation still suffices as long as the argument places of the predicate variables are occupied only by simple variables of the required type. It is different, however, when specialized predicates are substituted into the argument places.

For example, let F be a predicate variable of the type $((i))$, whose argument is thus any monadic predicate of individuals. Further, let G be a variable for dyadic predicates of individuals. With G we can form the following predicates of the variable x: $G(x, x)$, $G(x, y)$, and $G(y, x)$, where the latter two predicates contain the parameter y. We are not able without further conventions to express directly that F holds for any particular one of these predicates. For if we were to write, say, $F(G)$, then it would not be clear which of the monadic predicates is to be understood by G. It is easiest to use a roundabout device. Let us introduce a predicate variable H of type (i). Then the formulas

$$(EH)\,(F(H)\,\&\,(x)\,(H(x)\sim G(x,x))),$$
$$(EH)\,(F(H)\,\&\,(x)\,(H(x)\sim G(x,y))),$$
$$(EH)\,(F(H)\,\&\,(x)\,(H(x)\sim G(y,x))),$$

or the formulas

$$(H)\,((x)\,(H(x)\sim G(x,x))\rightarrow F(H)),$$
$$(H)\,((x)\,(H(x)\sim G(x,y))\rightarrow F(H)),$$
$$(H)\,((x)\,(H(x)\sim G(y,x))\rightarrow F(H))$$

may be used as substitutes to remedy our inability to express the fact that F holds for the above three predicates.

There is also, to be sure, the possibility of so constructing the formalism that one can get along without that sort of device. The advantage is then that the Rule of Substitution for Predicate Variables (the analogue of Rule $a3$) of the restricted predicate calculus) is not lost, and the axiomatic construction of the calculus of order ω can be made in complete analogy with the construction of the restricted predicate calculus, a construction with which we are familiar. We would then, however, have to pay for this with a more complicated notation. In the case discussed above, we can proceed by adding an individual variable, say x, as a subscript to the variable F. We then have in

$$F_x(G(x,x))\,;\quad F_x(G(x,y))\,;\quad F_x(G(y,x))$$

the symbolic expression for the three sentences mentioned. The variable x is a bound variable in the three formulas, and may therefore be replaced by another variable of the same sort. For example, the formulas

$$F_z(G(z,z))\,;\quad F_z(G(z,y))\,;\quad F_z(G(y,z))$$

have the same meaning as the above formulas.

If we wish to make use of this subscript notation in full generality, then every predicate variable of second or higher level must be given a subscript. Let F be such an n-adic predicate variable. Let $G_1, G_2, \ldots, G_n$ be variables that may be arguments of F. If individual variables occur among them, we omit them. Let

$$H_{11}, \ldots, H_{1 i_1}; \quad H_{21}, \ldots, H_{2 i_2}; \quad \ldots; \quad H_{n_1}, \ldots, H_{n i_n}$$

be variables such that $H_{k1}, \ldots, H_{k i_k}$ may be arguments of G_k ($k = 1, \ldots, n$). To F is then assigned the subscript as exhibited in

$$F_{[H_{11}, \ldots, H_{1 i_1}; \quad H_{21}, \ldots, H_{2 i_2}; \quad \ldots; \quad H_{n_1}, \ldots, H_{n i_n}]}.$$

The same holds for predicate constants. We give several examples. Instead of $\mathrm{Sym}(R)$ we would now have to write $\mathrm{Sym}_{xy}(R(x, y))$; and instead of $\mathrm{Imp}(F, G)$, $\mathrm{Imp}_{xy}(F(x), G(y))$. Instead of the formula $\mathfrak{N}(\Phi)$ used in § 2, we would have to write $\mathfrak{N}_F(\Phi(F))$, where F is of type (i). We see from this that the symbolism is considerably burdened by the subscript notation. In what follows we shall therefore use the simpler notation, and only occasionally refer to the subscript notation.

We turn now to the question of the axiom system for the universally valid formulas. First of all, the concept of formula must be defined. This may be done in the same way as above for the restricted predicate calculus, by means of Rules 1) through 5) of Chapter 3, § 4, bearing in mind, however, that now we have more kinds of variables. As to the axiom system itself, no system can be found which yields all universally valid formulas without exception.[1] Nevertheless, the axiom system which follows should hardly ever fail, even for complicated modes of inference, such as are used, say, in mathematical analysis (cf. the discussion of the following section). This system is essentially only a generalization of the system set up earlier for the restricted predicate calculus.

The system is constructed in the following way:

---

[1] This follows from the paper of K. Gödel already cited in § 1 of this chapter.

I. To begin with, we again use, as primitive formulas, formulas a) through d) of the sentential calculus, given in Chapter 3, § 5.

II. To the primitive formulas e) and f) of the restricted predicate calculus, there corresponds the following rule for constructing primitive formulas: Let G and H be variables of any type a whatsoever, and F be one of type (a). Then every formula

(II, 1) $$(G) F(G) \to F(H)$$

and every formula

(II, 2) $$F(H) \to (EG) F(G)$$

is a primitive formula. (We include here the case where G is of type i, and hence is an individual variable.)

III. There is further a special group of axioms for the extended predicate calculus which correspond to the axiom of choice of set theory and which constitute a generalization of Axiom g) set up above for the calculus of second order. Let F be a variable of any type a; G and L variables of any type b; A and H variables of type (a, b); and T one of type (b). Then,

(III)
$$(EH) \{ (F) [(EG) A(F, G) \to (EG) (H(F, G) \,\&\, A(F, G))]$$
$$\&\, (F) (G) (L) [(H(F, G) \,\&\, H(F, L)) \to (T) (T(G) \sim T(L))] \}$$

is a primitive formula.

IV. Further, let $L_1, L_2, \ldots, L_n$ be variables of types $b_1, b_2, \ldots, b_n$ respectively; G and H variables of type $(b_1, b_2, \ldots, b_n)$, and A one of type $((b_1, b_2, \ldots, b_n))$. Then

(IV) $(L_1) \ldots (L_n) [G(L_1, \ldots, L_n)$
$$\sim H(L_1, \ldots, L_n)] \to (A(G) \to A(H))$$

is a primitive formula. (These "axioms of extensionality" correspond to the identity condition of set theory.

The rules for deducing new formulas are analogous to those of the predicate calculus. $a1)$ and $\beta)$ remain unchanged. Rules $a2)$, $\gamma 1)$, and $\gamma 2)$ must be modified to take into account that we now have more types of variables. The extension of $a2$) cannot, however, entirely make up for the former Rule $a3$). The system of primitive formulas must therefore be extended still further in the following way.

Let $G_1, G_2, \ldots, G_n$ be variables of types $a_1, a_2, \ldots, a_n$ respectively; let F be a variable of type $(a_1, a_2, \ldots, a_n)$; and let $\mathfrak{A}(G_1, G_2, \ldots, G_n)$ be a formula containing the free variables $G_1, G_2, \ldots, G_n$. Then every formula of the form

$$(V) \quad (EF)(G_1) \ldots (G_n)(F(G_1, \ldots, G_n) \sim \mathfrak{A}(G_1, \ldots, G_n))$$

is a primitive formula. These formulas (V) serve, in deducing new formulas, to substitute a predicate variable for a formula with free variables, which, as we have seen (§ 2), constitutes the definition of a predicate constant.

If we use the subscript notation, we can dispense with formulas (V). In that case, the generalization of Rule $a3$) of the restricted predicate calculus is added to the Rules of Inference, and formulas (V) are then provable.

Another procedure, besides the one followed here for constructing the calculus of order ω, is to use consistently only monadic predicates of the various levels in the formal construction. For, by results due to Kuratowski,[1] we may, for instance, regard a dyadic predicate of individuals as a monadic predicate in the domain of ordered pairs (x, y). The ordered pair (x, y) is defined (if for convenience we use the terminology of set theory) as the set which contains as elements only the two following sets: the set with x as its only element, and the set with x and y as its only elements. For the definition of these sets, or their corresponding predicates, only the dyadic predicate of identity is required, and this is also reducible to monadic predicates (cf. § 1 of this chapter). We have not followed this method here in the calculus of order ω because it makes a predicate $F(x, y)$ of individuals, which otherwise is of first level, into a predicate of relatively high level. But otherwise the limitation to monadic predicates has many formal advantages.

---

[1] C. Kuratowski, *Sur la notion de l'ordre dans la théorie des ensembles.* Fund. Math. Vol. 2 (1921).

The consistency of the calculus of order ω can be proved in a simple way by an extension of the method used in Chapter 3, § 9.[1]

§ 6. Applications of the Calculus of Order ω

The calculus of order ω can be used for the derivation of consequences from the axioms of any given theory in the same way as was set forth in detail for the restricted predicate calculus in Chapter 3, § 11.

Compared to the restricted predicate calculus, we then have more extended means of expression with respect to axioms and consequences. We shall illustrate this application of the calculus of order ω by an example.

For this we shall take *the foundation of the theory of real numbers.* Here the real numbers will not be introduced by an axiom system of their own but will be reduced to the rational numbers. Thus we take the class of rational numbers as the domain of individuals, and assume that suitable axioms have been introduced for the basic arithmetical relations such as addition, subtraction, the relation of being larger than, etc., in the domain of rational numbers. In mathematics, various methods of reducing the real numbers to the rational numbers are used. For example, one may define a real number by means of a Cantor fundamental sequence, or by an infinite binary or decimal fraction. Dedekind's method is the most suitable for use in connection with logic.

According to Dedekind, we define a real number as a "cut"; *i.e.,* as a division of the rational numbers into two classes with the following properties:

1. Each of the two classes contains at least one rational number.

2. In the first class there is no greatest rational number.

---

[1] Cf. A. Tarski, *Einige Betrachtungen über die Begriffe der ω-Widerspruchsfreiheit und der ω-Vollständigkeit.* Mh. Math. Physik Vol. 40 (1933), and G. Gentzen, *Die Widerspruchfreiheit der Stufenlogik.* Math Z. Vol. 41 (1936). Gentzen uses the construction of the calculus of order ω just discussed, in which only monadic predicates occur. To carry over his method to our axiom system involves no special difficulties.

3. If a rational number belongs to the first class, then all smaller rational numbers also belong to the first class.

Now in any such division, we need consider only the first of the two classes, and are then dealing with a set of rational numbers, which may be given by means of a defining predicate.

By a real number we now understand a set of rational numbers for which there is a defining predicate P that satisfies the following three conditions:

1. $(Ex)P(x) \& (Ex)\overline{P}(x)$.

("The two classes determined by $P(x)$ and $\overline{P}(x)$ are both not empty.")

2. $(x)\{P(x) \to (Ey)[<(x, y) \& P(y)]\}$.

("For each rational number having the property P, there is a larger one which likewise has the property P.")

3. $(x)\{P(x) \to (y)[<(y, x) \to P(y)]\}$.

("If x has the property P, then all smaller rational numbers y also have the property P.")

These three conditions together—we may think of them as being joined by the sign &—represent the property, pertaining to a predicate, of defining a cut. This property of a predicate will be designated by $Ct(P)$. Two predicates P and Q with the properties $Ct(P)$ and $Ct(Q)$ define the same real number if and only if the sets which correspond to P and Q are identical, *i.e.*, if $Eq(P, Q)$ holds.

Now we can introduce first the ordering relation for the real numbers. For two predicates P and Q with the property Ct, we define $\leqq(P, Q)$ to mean the same as $Imp(P, Q)$, *i.e.*, as

$$(x)(P(x) \to Q(x)) ;$$

or in symbols:

$$Ct(P) \& Ct(Q) \to [Imp(P, Q) \sim \leqq(P, Q)].$$

The statement $<(P, Q)$ will then be defined by

$$Ct(P) \& Ct(Q) \to [<(P, Q) \sim (Imp(P, Q) \& \overline{Eq}(P, Q))].$$

It can then be proved in our calculus that the two relations $\leqq(P, Q)$ and $<(P, Q)$ are transitive. All the other properties characteristic of an ordering relation can be derived similarly.

The addition and multiplication of real numbers can be reduced to the addition and multiplication of rational numbers. The predicate

$$(Ey)\,(Ez)\,[P\,(y)\,\&\,Q\,(z)\,\&\,(x = y + z)\,]$$

defines the sum, the predicate

$$(Ey)\,(Ez)\,[P\,(y)\,\&\,Q\,(z)\,\&\,(x = y \cdot z)\,]$$

defines the product, of the real numbers defined by P and Q. ($x = y + z$ and $x = y \cdot z$ are here basic triadic predicates in the domain of rational numbers.)

We are now in a position to introduce in the customary manner the concepts of the *boundedness* and of the *least upper bound* of a set of real numbers. A set of real numbers is given by a predicate of predicates $A\,(P)$ satisfying the condition:

$$(P)\,[A\,(P) \to \mathrm{Ct}\,(P)\,]\,\&\,(P)\,(Q)\,\{\,[A\,(P)\,\&\,\mathrm{Eq}\,(P, Q)\,] \to A\,(Q)\,\}.$$

For a set $A\,(P)$ of real numbers to be bounded from above means that there exists a real number which is either greater than or equal to every number of the set; in symbols:

$$(EP)\,\{\mathrm{Ct}\,(P)\,\&\,(Q)\,[A\,(Q) \to\, \leqq (Q, P)\,]\,\},$$

which we abbreviate by $(EP)\,\mathrm{Bd}\,(P, A)$; in words, there is a number P which constitutes an upper bound of the set A.

We shall also assume that $A\,(P)$ contains at least one element; that is, that the formula

$$(EP)\,A\,(P)$$

holds. The theorem regarding the upper bound may now be formulated thus: *If a set of real numbers has an upper bound, then it also has a least upper bound.*

The mathematical proof for the existence of the least upper bound, reduced to its simplest form, consists in forming the union of the set of real numbers considered (which is a set of first-level sets). In accordance with the remarks of § 3 of this chapter, the union associated with $A\,(P)$ is given by the predicate

$$(EP)\,(P\,(x)\,\&\,A\,(P)\,).$$

We will abbreviate this predicate by $\mathrm{Un}(x, A)$.

Thus our task is to show that the predicate $\mathrm{Un}(x, A)$ gives a real number which constitutes the least upper bound of the set A.

To begin with, we must show that the set determined by $\mathrm{Un}(x, A)$ actually is a real number.

It can easily be shown first that the three properties of Ct hold for Un. We give the proof for the first property.

From
$$(EP)A(P)$$
and
$$(P)(A(P) \rightarrow \mathrm{Ct}(P)),$$
we infer
$$(EP)(\mathrm{Ct}(P) \,\&\, A(P)).$$
Since
$$\mathrm{Ct}(P) \rightarrow (Ex)P(x)$$
holds, we have
$$(EP)((Ex)P(x) \,\&\, A(P)).$$
The last formula can be transformed into
$$(Ex)(EP)(P(x) \,\&\, A(P)),$$
that is,
$$(Ex)\,\mathrm{Un}(x, A).$$
Similarly it can be shown that
$$(Ex)\overline{\mathrm{Un}}(x, A), \quad i.e., \quad (Ex)\,\overline{(EP)}\,(P(x) \,\&\, A(P)).$$
This formula may first be transformed into
$$(Ex)(P)(A(P) \rightarrow \overline{P}(x)).$$
We now have, by the assumption of boundedness of the set A,
$$(EP)\{\mathrm{Ct}(P) \,\&\, (Q)[A(Q) \rightarrow\, \leqq(Q, P)]\}.$$
Furthermore,
$$\mathrm{Ct}(P) \rightarrow (Ex)\overline{P}(x)$$
holds. Therefore
$$(EP)\{(Ex)\overline{P}(x) \,\&\, \mathrm{Ct}(P) \,\&\, (Q)[A(Q) \rightarrow\, \leqq(Q, P)]\}.$$

From the definition of $\leqq (Q, P)$ it follows easily that

$$\leqq (Q, P) \,\&\, \mathrm{Ct}(Q) \,\&\, \mathrm{Ct}(P) \to (x)\,(\overline{P}(x) \to \overline{Q}(x)).$$

We may hence replace

$$(Q)\,[A(Q) \to \leqq (Q, P)]$$

in the next to the last formula by

$$(Q)\,[A(Q) \to (x)\,(\overline{P}(x) \to \overline{Q}(x))]$$

or by

$$(x)\,\{\overline{P}(x) \to (Q)\,[A(Q) \to \overline{Q}(x)]\}.$$

From the formula:

$$(EP)\,\{(Ex)\overline{P}(x) \,\&\, \mathrm{Ct}(P) \,\&\, (x)\,[\overline{P}(x) \to (Q)\,(A(Q) \to \overline{Q}(x))]\}$$

we then obtain

$$(Ex)\,(Q)\,(A(Q) \to \overline{Q}(x)),$$

i.e.

$$(Ex)\,\overline{\mathrm{Un}}(x, A).$$

Hence the first property of cuts is proved for $\mathrm{Un}(x, A)$.

In an analogous manner properties 2. and 3. of cuts are proved for $\mathrm{Un}(x, A)$, whence $\mathrm{Ct}(\mathrm{Un})$ holds.

We shall now show

$$(P)\,(A(P) \to \leqq (P, \mathrm{Un})),$$

i.e. the real number corresponding to Un *is an upper bound for the set determined by* $A(P)$.

If we substitute the defining expressions for Un and $\leqq$, then this formula becomes

$$(P)\,\{A(P) \to (x)\,[P(x) \to (EQ)\,(Q(x) \,\&\, A(Q))]\},$$

which can be transformed into

$$(P)\,(x)\,[A(P) \,\&\, P(x) \to (EQ)\,(A(Q) \,\&\, Q(x))].$$

The last form enables us to recognize the formula as an application of Axiom (II, 2), page 156.

It still remains to be shown that $\mathrm{Un}(x, A)$ is the *least* upper bound, or, in symbols,

$$(P)\{[\mathrm{Ct}(P) \& (Q)(A(Q) \to \leqq (Q, P))] \to \leqq (\mathrm{Un}, P)\}.$$

If here again we replace all abbreviations by their definitions, we obtain

$$(P)\{[\mathrm{Ct}(P) \& (Q)[A(Q) \to (x)(Q(x) \to P(x))]]$$
$$\to (y)[(EP')(P'(y) \& A(P')) \to P(y)]\}.$$

The universal quantifier (x) may here be shifted to the left, and we thus obtain

$$(P)\{[\mathrm{Ct}(P) \& (x)(Q)[A(Q) \& Q(x) \to P(x)]]$$
$$\to (y)(EP')[P'(y) \& A(P') \to P(y)]\}.$$

This formula can be proved by means of the generalization of Theorem 22, page 72.

The examples given should be sufficient to show that the calculus of order ω is the appropriate means for expressing the modes of inference of mathematical analysis. A complete construction of the foundations of mathematics by means of the calculus of order ω has been given by Whitehead and Russell,[1] although their discussion is unnecessarily complicated by the use of the ramified theory of types, mentioned in § 4. However, to make their deductions independent of that theory does not involve any special difficulties.

---

[1] A. N. Whitehead and B. Russell, *Principia Mathematica*, 2nd ed. (Cambridge, 1925-1927).

EDITOR'S NOTES

NOTE 1. The designation "sentential calculus" has been adopted in this translation rather than the (perhaps more usual) designation "propositional calculus" because it is terminologically coordinate with the name "predicate calculus," which it would seem somewhat arbitrary not to use in translating the German *"Prädikatenkalkül"* of the second and subsequent chapters. There are in general two possible ways of forming the name of a particular calculus: (1) by reference to linguistic expressions or symbols and (2) by reference to objective, non-linguistic entities. Thus the names "sentential calculus" and "predicate calculus" are examples of the first of these ways, since they refer respectively to sentences and predicates, which are kinds of linguistic expressions. On the other hand, the names "propositional calculus" and "functional calculus" (the latter corresponding to "predicate calculus" and perhaps now the more usual title) might be taken as examples of the second of the two ways of naming a calculus, since they refer respectively to propositions and functions, which many (though by no means all) logicians consider to be objective, non-linguistic entities.

The question whether in addition to sentences there exist *propositions* in the sense of non-linguistic abstract objects such that each of them may be expressed by a sentence of which it then constitutes the meaning, and the analogous question concerning predicates and functions are among the most difficult and currently most controverted questions in the theory of logic. They are, however, questions on which the foregoing text does not pronounce, and which it is beyond the scope of the text and also beyond the scope of these notes to discuss in detail. Fortunately, for the immediate purposes of the text these questions need not be decided, and of course no decision is implied in the mere use of the designations "sentential calculus" and "predicate calculus." All that the student need be concerned to keep in mind in this connection for immediate purposes is that the sentential variables "X," "Y," etc. are, in the intended interpretation of the sentential calculus, to be regarded as standing for, or as replaceable by, (declarative) sentences, and similarly that in the intended interpretation of the predicate calculus the predicate variables "F," "G," etc. are to be regarded as standing for, or as replaceable by, expressions for properties (or for the corresponding classes) or for relations.

NOTE 2. The reader who has little acquaintance with logic texts must be warned that the set of symbols introduced here for the fundamental logical connectives is by no means in universal or standard use. Thus the tilde, which is introduced in the present text as the connective of (material) equivalence (*i.e.* agreement in truth value), is in many texts used as the sign of negation. It is therefore necessary for the student who wishes to read widely in the literature of logic to acquire a certain facility in passing from one symbolism to an alternative one, but this ordinarily occasions little difficulty. The like is true also as regards terminological usages in the field of logic.

NOTE 3. A wider use than is to be found in the present text may be made of the method of truth tables, briefly indicated in § 2, as a means of determining whether or not a given sentential combination, or truth function, is logically true. This method consists, to describe it as shortly as possible, in assigning systematically every possible distribution of truth values, represented by "T" and "F," to the ultimate components of the given sentential formula and then applying the truth tables for the fundamental connectives (*i.e.* the truth tables which are introduced in § 1, and may be regarded as *defining* the fundamental connectives) to determine for each of the possible value distributions the truth value of progressively larger components until finally the truth value of the given formula as a whole is determined. A sentential formula which yields the value truth for every possible assignment of truth values to its ultimate components is thereby verified as logically true, and one which always yields the value falsehood is thereby determined as logically false. Thus the truth table constitutes an effective method for testing the validity of formulas of the sentential calculus and is, as the reader will readily perceive, entirely equivalent to the method of normal forms, which is preferred by Hilbert and Ackermann and is employed in the present text.

In connection with the method of truth tables there is an important terminological usage to which the attention of the beginning student in logic should be called. A formula of the sentential calculus found by the truth-table method to be logically true is now customarily called a *tautology* and one found to be logically false is called a *contradiction*, the terms being taken from L. Wittgenstein (1921). And now we may say, in view of the equivalence of the method of truth tables and that of normal forms and in view of the considerations adduced in the final paragraph of Chapter I, § 11, that in the sentential calculus every theorem is a tautology and every tautology is a theorem. It should be remarked, however, that the application of the term "tautology" to logical truths beyond the domain of the sentential calculus is highly questionable and had perhaps better be avoided altogether.

NOTE 4. In their discussion of the Principle of Duality the authors fail to make the use of the term *dual* quite clear. The following definition may therefore prove useful to the reader.

If $\mathfrak{A}$ is an expression formed from elementary sentences and their negations by means solely of conjunction and disjunction, the result of interchanging "&" and "v" throughout $\mathfrak{A}$ is called the *dual* of $\mathfrak{A}$. Thus, in the first example given in Chapter I, § 5 to illustrate the Principle of Duality, "$X \& YZ$" is the dual of "$X(Y \& Z)$," and "$(X \& Y)(X \& Z)$" is the dual of "$XY \& XZ$." It should be noted that the same formula $\mathfrak{A}$ may have different duals, according to which particular rendering of $\mathfrak{A}$ is used; but it is easily seen that any two duals of the same formula $\mathfrak{A}$ must be equivalent. The reader should also encounter no difficulty in proving for himself that if $\mathfrak{A}$ is a theorem, then the negation of its dual is also a theorem.

The definition of the dual of a formula belonging to the restricted predicate calculus is analogous to the foregoing definition, and is obvious from the discussion at the beginning of § 8 of Chapter III. It may then be proved for the restricted predicate calculus also that if a formula 𝔄 is a theorem, the negation of its dual is also a theorem.

NOTE 5. In Chapter II the translation follows the original text in employing the term "judgment" ("*Urteil*") in the discussion of the traditional logic derived from Aristotle. Since this term has almost entirely passed out of use in modern logic, it perhaps requires a few words of supplementary explanation here. A judgment was traditionally conceived to be the intellectual content or meaning expressed by a sentence and thus was supposed to be a non-linguistic entity. To this extent the term "judgment" bears some analogy to the present-day term "proposition," in the use explained in Note 1. But there is the very important difference that a judgment was considered to be somewhat psychological in character, being in some sense an act of the mind; whereas those modern logicians who accept the existence of propositions consider them to be non-mental and non-subjective, as well as non-linguistic, entities. It is unfortunate that the term "proposition" itself was used by traditional logicians, in a sense antithetical to that which it now has, to mean the linguistic expression of a judgment, *i.e.* a sentence.

NOTE 6. The distinction between variables and constants, which appears prominently in Chapter III § 11 and subsequently, is sometimes difficult for the beginner to grasp clearly. It is not always understood that a constant, like a variable, is a *symbol*, a linguistic expression, but with the important distinction that a constant has a fixed designation, which remains unaltered throughout the discussion in which the constant appears; whereas a variable designates ambiguously, so to speak, assuming any one of a range of values. It would, however, be a grave error to suppose that the distinction between variables and constants reflects a corresponding distinction in the domain of objects to which the variables and constants alike refer. Thus to assert with reference, say, to real number theory that the variables "x" and "y" designate variable numbers, whereas such constants as "2" and "π" designate constant numbers, would be nonsense; or at least there is no known intelligible theory which could accommodate so odd a notion as that of a variable number.

BIBLIOGRAPHY

Of the *introductory* *books* on mathematical logic, we mention the following:

BEHMANN, H., *Mathematik und Logik*, Leipzig 1927.

CARNAP, R., *Abriss der Logistik*, Vienna 1929.

CHURCH, A., *Introduction to Mathematical Logic*, Princeton 1944.

COOLEY, J., *A Primer of Formal Logic*, New York 1942.

COUTURAT, L., *L'Algèbre de la Logique*, Paris 1905.

LEWIS, C. I. and C. H. LANGFORD, *Symbolic Logic*, New York 1932.

QUINE, W. V., *A System of Logistic*, Cambridge (Mass.) 1934.

— *Elementary Logic*, Boston 1941.

RUSSELL, B., *Introduction to Mathematical Philosophy*, 2nd ed., London 1920.

TARSKI, A., *Introduction to Logic*, New York 1941.

WHITEHEAD, A. N. and RUSSELL, B.: Introduction to the *Principia Mathematica*, Cambridge Univ. Press 1925.

Of the *more comprehensive works* on the subject, we list the following:

CARNAP, R., *Logical Syntax of Language*, London and New York 1937.

— *Introduction to Semantics*, Cambridge (Mass.) 1942.

— *Formalization of Logic*, Cambridge (Mass.) 1943.

— *Meaning and Necessity*, Chicago, 1947.

HILBERT, D. and BERNAYS, P., *Grundlagen der Mathematik*, Vols. I and II, Berlin 1934 and 1939.

QUINE, W. V., *Mathematical Logic*, New York 1940.

RUSSELL, B., *Principles of Mathematics*, 2nd ed., London 1937.

WHITEHEAD, A. N. and RUSSELL, B., *Principia Mathematica*, 2nd ed., Vols. I (1925), II (1927) and III (1927), Cambridge Univ. Press.

Of *older* works which are still of interest, we name the following:

FREGE, G., *Begriffsschrift. Eine der arithmetischen nachgebildete Formelsprache des reinen Denkens*, Halle 1879.

— *Die Grundlagen der Arithmetik. Eine logisch-mathematische Untersuchung über den Begriff der Zahl*, Breslau 1884.

— *Grundgesetze der Arithmetik, begriffsschriftlich abgeleitet*, Jena 1893-1903.

PEANO, G., *Notations de logique mathématique; introduction au Formulaire de Mathématiques*, Turin 1894.

— *Formulaire de Mathématiques*, 1895-1905.

PEIRCE, C. S., *Collected Papers*, edited by C. Hartshorne and P. Weiss, Cambridge (Mass.).

SCHRÖDER, E., *Vorlesungen über die Algebra der Logik (exakte Logik)*, 3 vols., Leipzig 1890-1905.

For those questions of *set theory* which are closely connected with logic, we refer to

FRAENKEL, A., *Einleitung in die Mengenlehre*, 3rd ed., Berlin 1928. [*Reprint*, New York 1946.]

We can not give here a complete bibliography of the literature of logic, which is very extensive. For a complete chronological list of literature on the subject up to the year 1935, we refer to the following valuable work:

CHURCH, A., *A Bibliography of Symbolic Logic*, The Journal of Symbolic Logic, Vol. I, pp. 121-128. Vol. III, pp. 178 - 212.

INDEX

(Numbers refer to pages)

171

CHELSEA

SCIENTIFIC

BOOKS

THE THEORY OF MATRICES
By F. R. GANTMACHER

This treatise, by one of Russia's leading mathematicians gives, in easily accessible form, a coherent account of matrix theory with a view to applications in mathematics, theoretical physics, statistics, electrical engineering, etc. The individual chapters have been kept as far as possible independent of each other, so that the reader acquainted with the contents of Chapter I can proceed immediately to the chapters that especially interest him. Much of the material has been available until now only in the periodical literature.

Partial Contents. VOL. ONE. I. Matrices and Matrix Operations. II. The Algorithm of Gauss and Applications. III. Linear Operators in an n-Dimensional Vector Space. IV. Characteristic Polynomial and Minimal Polynomial of a Matrix (Generalized Bézout Theorem, Method of Faddeev for Simultaneous Computation of Coefficients of Characteristic Polynomial and Adjoint Matrix, . . .). V. Functions of Matrices (Various Forms of the Definition, Components, Application to Integration of System of Linear Differential Eqns, Stability of Motion, . . .). VI. Equivalent Transformations of Polynomial Matrices; Analytic Theory of Elementary Divisors. VII. The Structure of a Linear Operator in an n-Dimensional Space (Minimal Polynomial, Congruence, Factor Space, Jordan Form, Krylov's Method of Transforming Secular Eqn, . . .). VIII. Matrix Equations (Matrix Polynomial Eqns, Roots and Logarithm of Matrices, . . .). IX. Linear Operators in a Unitary Space. X. Quadratic and Hermitian Forms.

VOL. TWO. XI. Complex Symmetric, Skew-symmetric, and Orthogonal Matrices. XII. Singular Pencils of Matrices. XIII. Matrices with Non-Negative Elements (Gen'l and Spectral Properties, Reducible M's, Primitive and Imprimitive M's, Stochastic M's, Totally Non-Negative M's, . . .). XIV. Applications of the Theory of Matrices to the Investigation of Systems of Linear Differential Equations. XV. The Problem of Routh-Hurwitz and Related Questions (Routh's Algorithm, Lyapunov's Theorem, Infinite Hankel M's, Supplements to Routh-Hurwitz Theorem, Stability Criterion of Liénard and Chipart, Hurwitz Polynomials, Stieltjes' Theorem, Domain of Stability, Markov Parameters, Problem of Moments, Markov and Chebyshev Theorems, Generalized Routh-Hurwitz Problem, . . .). BIBLIOGRAPHY.

—Vol. I. 1960. x + 374 pp. 6x9.　　　　[131]　**$6.00**
—Vol. II. 1960. x + 277 pp. 6x9.　　　　[133]　**$6.00**

UNTERSUCHUNGEN UEBER HOEHERE ARITHMETIK
By C. F. GAUSS

A reprint of the 1889 German translation of Gauss's *Disquisitiones Arithmeticae*, which contains a very extensive appendix, consisting of ten number-theoretical papers of Gauss, both published and posthumous.

—Reprint, 1965. xv + 695 pp. 6x9.　　　　[191]　**$8.75**

THEORY OF PROBABILITY
By B. V. GNEDENKO

This textbook, by Russia's leading probabilist, is suitable for senior undergraduate and first-year graduate courses. It covers, in highly readable form, a wide range of topics and, by carefully selected exercises and examples, keeps the reader throughout in close touch with problems in science and engineering.

The translation has been made from the fourth Russian edition by Prof. B. D. Seckler. Earlier editions have won wide and enthusiastic acceptance as a text at many leading colleges and universities.

"extremely well written . . . suitable for individual study . . . Gnedenko's book is a milestone in the writing on probability theory."—*Science.*

Partial Contents: I. The Concept of Probability (Various approaches to the definition. Space of Elementary Events. Classical Definition. Geometrical Probability. Relative Frequency. Axiomatic construction . . .). II. Sequences of Independent Trials. III Markov Chains IV. Random Variables and Distribution Functions (Continuous and discrete distributions. Multidimensional d. functions. Functions of random variables. Stieltjes integral). V. Numerical Characteristics of Random Variables (Mathematical expectation. Variance... Moments). VI. Law of Large Numbers (Mass phenomena. Tchebychev's form of law. Strong law of large numbers...). VII. Characteristic Functions (Properties. Inversion formula and uniqueness theorem. Helly's theorems. Limit theorems. Char. functs. for multidimensional random variables...). VIII. Classical Limit Theorem (Liapunov's theorem. Local limit theorem). IX. Theory of Infinitely Divisible Distribution Laws. X. Theory of Stochastic Processes (Generalized Markov equation. Continuous S. processes. Purely discontinuous S. processes. Kolmogorov-Feller equations. Homogeneous S. processes with independent increments. Stationary S. process. Stochastic integral. Spectral theorem of S. processes. Birkhoff-Khinchine ergodic theorem). XI. Elements of Queueing Theory (General characterization of the problems. Birth-and-death processes. Single-server queueing systems. Flows. Elements of the theory of stand-by systems). XII. Elements of Statistics (Problems. Variational series. Glivenko's Theorem and Kolmogorov's criterion. Two-sample problem. Critical region . . . Confidence limits). TABLES. BIBLIOGRAPHY. ANSWERS TO THE EXERCISES.

—4th ed. Summer, 1967. Approx. 500 pp. 6x9. [132]   **$9.50**

THE ALGEBRA OF INVARIANTS
By J. H. GRACE and A. YOUNG

An introductory account.

Partial Contents: I. Introduction. II. The Fundamental Theorem. III. Transvectants. V. Elementary Complete Systems. VI. Gordan's Theorem. VII. The Quintic. VIII. Simultaneous Systems. IX. Hilbert's Theorem. XI. Apolarity. XII. Ternary Forms. XV. Types of Covariants. XVI. General Theorems on Quantics. APPENDICES.

—1903-65. Repr. of 1st ed. vii+384 pp. 5x8.   [180]   **$4.95**

REELLE FUNKTIONEN. Punktfunktionen
By H. HAHN

—426 pp. 5½x8½. Orig. pub. at $12.80. [52] **$4.95**

ALGEBRAIC LOGIC
By P. R. HALMOS

"Algebraic Logic is a modern approach to some of the problems of mathematical logic, and the theory of polyadic Boolean algebras, with which this volume is mostly concerned, is intended to be an efficient way of treating algebraic logic in a unified manner.

"[The material] is accessible to a general mathematical audience; no vast knowledge of algebra or logic is required . . . Except for a slight Boolean foundation, the volume is essentially self-contained."—*From the Preface.*

—1962 271 pp. 6x9 [154] **$3.95**

LECTURES ON ERGODIC THEORY
By P. R. HALMOS

CONTENTS: Introduction. Recurrence. Mean Convergence. Pointwise Convergence. Ergodicity. Mixing. Measure Algebras. Discrete Spectrum. Automorphisms of Compact Groups. Generalized Proper Values. Weak Topology. Weak Approximation. Uniform Topology. Uniform Approximation. Category. Invariant Measures. Generalized Ergodic Theorems. Unsolved Problems.

"Written in the pleasant, relaxed, and clear style usually associated with the author. The material is organized very well and painlessly presented."
—*Bulletin of the A.M.S.*

—1960. (Repr. of 1956 ed.) viii + 101 pp. 5¼x8. [142] **$2.95**

INTRODUCTION TO HILBERT SPACE AND THE THEORY OF SPECTRAL MULTIPLICITY
By P. R. HALMOS

A clear, readable introductory treatment of Hilbert Space.

—1957. 2nd ed. (c. repr. of 1st ed.). 120 pp. 6x9. [82] **$3.25**

RAMANUJAN:
Twelve Lectures on His Life and Works
By G. H. HARDY

The book is somewhat more than an account of the mathematical work and personality of Ramanujan; it is one of the very few full-length books of "shop talk" by an important mathematician.

—1940-59. viii+236 pp. 6x9. [136] **$3.95**

GRUNDZUEGE DER MENGENLEHRE
By F. HAUSDORFF

Some of the topics in the Grundzüge omitted from later editions:

Symmetric Sets—Principle of Duality—most of the "Algebra" of Sets—most of the "Ordered Sets"—Partially Ordered Sets—Arbitrary Sets of Complexes—Normal Types—Initial and Final Ordering—Complexes of Real Numbers—General Topological Spaces—Euclidean Spaces—the Special Methods Applicable in the Euclidean plane—Jordan's separation Theorem—The Theory of Content and Measure—The Theory of the Lebesgue Integral.

—Repr. of original (1914) edition. 484 pp. 5¼x8. [61] **$6.00**

SET THEORY
By F. HAUSDORFF

Hausdorff's classic text-book is an inspiration and a delight. The translation is from the Third (latest) German edition.

"We wish to state without qualification that this is an indispensable book for all those interested in the theory of sets and the allied branches of real variable theory."—*Bulletin of A. M. S.*

—2nd ed. 1962. 352 pp. 6x9. [119] **$6.50**

VORLESUNGEN UEBER DIE THEORIE DER ALGEBRAISCHEN ZAHLEN
By E. HECKE

"An elegant and comprehensive account of the modern theory of algebraic numbers."
—*Bulletin of the A. M. S.*

—1923. 264 pp. 5½x8½. [46] **$4.95**

INTEGRALGLEICHUNGEN UND GLEICHUNGEN MIT UNENDLICHVIELEN UNBEKANNTEN
By E. HELLINGER and O. TOEPLITZ

"Indispensable to anybody who desires to penetrate deeply into this subject."—*Bulletin of A.M.S.*

—With a preface by E. Hilb. 1928. 286 pp. 5¼x8. [89] **$4.50**

THEORIE DER ALGEBRAISCHE FUNKTIONEN EINER VARIABELN
By K. HENSEL and G. LANDSBERG

Partial Contents: PART ONE (Chaps. 1-8): Algebraic Functions on a Riemann Surface. PART TWO (Chaps. 9-13): The Field of Algebraic Functions. PART THREE (Chaps. 14-22): Algebraic Divisors and the Riemann-Roch Theorem. PART FOUR (Chaps. 23-27): Algebraic Curves. PART FIVE (Chaps. 28-31): The Classes of Algebraic Curves. PART SIX (Chaps. 32-37): Algebraic Relations among Abelian Integrals. APPENDIX: Historical Development. Geometrical Methods. Arithmetical Methods.

—1902-65. xvi + 707 pp. 6x9. [179] **$9.50**

LECTURES ON
GENERAL ALGEBRA
By A. G. KUROSH

Translated from the Russian by PROFESSOR K. A. HIRSCH, with a special preface for this edition by PROFESSOR KUROSH.

Partial Contents: CHAP. I. Relations. II. Groups and Rings (Groupoids, Semigroups, Groups, Rings, Fields, . . . , Gaussian rings, Dedekind rings). III. Universal Algebras. Groups with Multi-operators (. . . Free universal algebras, Free products of groups). IV. Lattices (Complete lattices, Modular lattice, Schmidt-Ore Theorem, . . . , Distributive lattices). V. Operator Groups and Rings. Modules. Linear Algebras (. . . Free modules, Vector spaces over fields, Rings of linear transformations, . . . , Derivations, Differential rings). VI. Ordered and Topological Groups and Rings. Rings with a Valuation. BIBLIOGRAPHY.

—1965. 335 pp. 6x9.   [168] **$6.95**

DIFFERENTIAL AND INTEGRAL CALCULUS
By E. LANDAU

A masterpiece of rigor and clarity.

"And what a book it is! The marks of Landau's thoroughness and elegance, and of his undoubted authority, impress themselves on the reader at every turn, from the opening of the preface . . . to the closing of the final chapter.

"It is a book that all analysts . . . should possess . . . to see how a master of his craft like Landau presented the calculus when he was at the height of his power and reputation."

—*Mathematical Gazette.*

—3rd ed. 1965. 372 pp. 6x9.   [78] **$6.00**

HANDBUCH DER LEHRE VON DER
VERTEILUNG DER PRIMZAHLEN
By E. LANDAU

TWO VOLUMES IN ONE.

To Landau's monumental work on prime-number theory there has been added, in this edition, two of Landau's papers and an up-to-date guide to the work: an Appendix by Prof. Paul T. Bateman.

—2nd ed. 1953. 1,028 pp. 5⅜x8.   [96] 2 vols. in 1. **$14.00**

LANDAU, "Neuere Funktiontheorie," see Weyl

VORLESUNGEN UEBER ZAHLENTHEORIE
By E. LANDAU

The various sections of this important work (Additive, Analytic, Geometric, and Algebraic Number Theory) can be read independently of one another.

—Vol. I, Pt. 2. *(Additive Number Theory) xii + 180 pp. Vol. II. (Analytical Number Theory and Geometrical Number Theory) viii + 308 pp. Vol. III. (Algebraic Number Theory and Fermat's Last Theorem) viii + 341 pp. 5¼x8¼. *(Vol. I, Pt. 1 is issued as **Elementare Zahlentheorie** (in German) or as **Elementary Number Theory** (in English). Orig. publ. at $26.40. [32] Three Vols. in one.   **$14.00**

GRUNDLAGEN DER ANALYSIS
By E. LANDAU

The student who wishes to study mathematical German will find Landau's famous *Grundlagen der Analysis* ideally suited to his needs.

Only a few score of German words will enable him to read the entire book with only an occasional glance at the Vocabulary! [A COMPLETE German-English vocabulary, prepared with the novice especially in mind, has been appended to the book.]

—4th ed. 1965. 173 pp. 5½x8½. [24] Cloth **$3.50**
[141] Paper **$1.95**

FOUNDATIONS OF ANALYSIS
By E. LANDAU

"Certainly no clearer treatment of the foundations of the number system can be offered. . . . One can only be thankful to the author for this fundamental piece of exposition, which is alive with his vitality and genius."—*J. F. Ritt, Amer. Math. Monthly.*

—2nd ed. 1960. 6x9. [79] **$3.95**

ELEMENTARE ZAHLENTHEORIE
By E. LANDAU

"Interest is enlisted at once and sustained by the accuracy, skill, and enthusiasm with which Landau marshals . . . facts and simplifies . . . details."
—*G. D. Birkhoff, Bulletin of the A. M. S.*

—1927-50. vii+180+iv pp. 5½x8½. [26] **$4.50**

ELEMENTARY NUMBER THEORY
By E. LANDAU

The present work is a translation of Prof. Landau's famous *Elementare Zahlentheorie*, with added exercises by Prof. Paul T. Bateman.

—2nd ed. 1966. 256 pp. 6x9. [125] **$4.95**

Einführung in die Elementare und Analytische Theorie der ALGEBRAISCHE ZAHLEN
By E. LANDAU

—2nd ed. vii + 147 pp. 5½x8. [62] **$2.95**

Mémoires sur la Théorie des SYSTEMES DES EQUATIONS DIFFERENTIELLES LINEAIRES, Vols. I, II, III
By J. A. LAPPO-DANILEVSKII

THREE VOLUMES IN ONE.

A reprint, in one volume, of Volumes 6, 7, and 8 of the works of the Stecklov Institute of Mathematics in Moscow.

"The theory of [systems of linear differential equations] is treated with elegance and generality by the author, and his contributions constitute an important addition to the field of differential equations."—*Applied Mechanics Reviews.*

—3 vols. in one. 1934; 1935; 1936. 689 pp. 5¼x8. [94] **$10.00**

SET TOPOLOGY
By R. VAIDYANATHASWAMY

In this text on Topology, the first edition of which was published in India, the concept of partial order has been made the unifying theme.

Over 500 exercises for the reader enrich the text.

CHAPTER HEADINGS: I. Algebra of Subsets of a Set. II. Rings and Fields of Sets. III. Algebra of Partial Order. IV. The Closure Function. V. Neighborhood Topology. VI. Open and Closed Sets. VII. Topological Maps. VIII. The Derived Set in T_1 Space. IX. The Topological Product. X. Convergence in Metrical Space. XI. Convergence Topology.

—2nd ed. 1960. vi + 305 pp. 6x9.   [139] **$6.00**

LECTURES ON THE GENERAL THEORY OF INTEGRAL FUNCTIONS
By G. VALIRON

—1923. xii + 208 pp. 5¼x8.   [56] **$3.50**

GRUPPEN VON LINEAREN TRANSFORMATIONEN
By B. L. VAN DER WAERDEN

—(Ergeb. der Math.) 1935. 94 pp. 5½x8½.   [45] **$2.50**

THE LOGIC OF CHANCE
By J. VENN

One of the classics of the theory of probability. Venn's book remains unsurpassed for clarity, readability, and sheer charm of exposition. No mathematics is required.

CONTENTS: PART ONE: Physical Foundations of the Science of Probability. CHAP. I. The Series of Probability. II. Formation of the Series, III. Origin, or Causation, of the Series. IV. How to Discover and Prove the Series. V. The Concept of Randomness. PART TWO: Logical Superstructure on the Above Physical Foundations. VI. Gradations of Belief. VII. The Rules of Inference in Probability. VIII. The Rule of Succession. IX. Induction. X. Causation and Design. XI. Material and Formal Logic . . . XIV. Fallacies. PART THREE: Applications. XV. Insurance and Gambling. XVI. Application to Testimony. XVII. Credibility of Extraordinary Stories. XVIII. The Nature and Use of an Average as a Means of Approximation to the Truth.

—Repr. of 3rd ed. xxix+508 pp. 5⅜x8.   [173]   Cloth **$4.95**
                                        [169]   Paper **$2.25**